Usborne

Thousands of Things to Spot

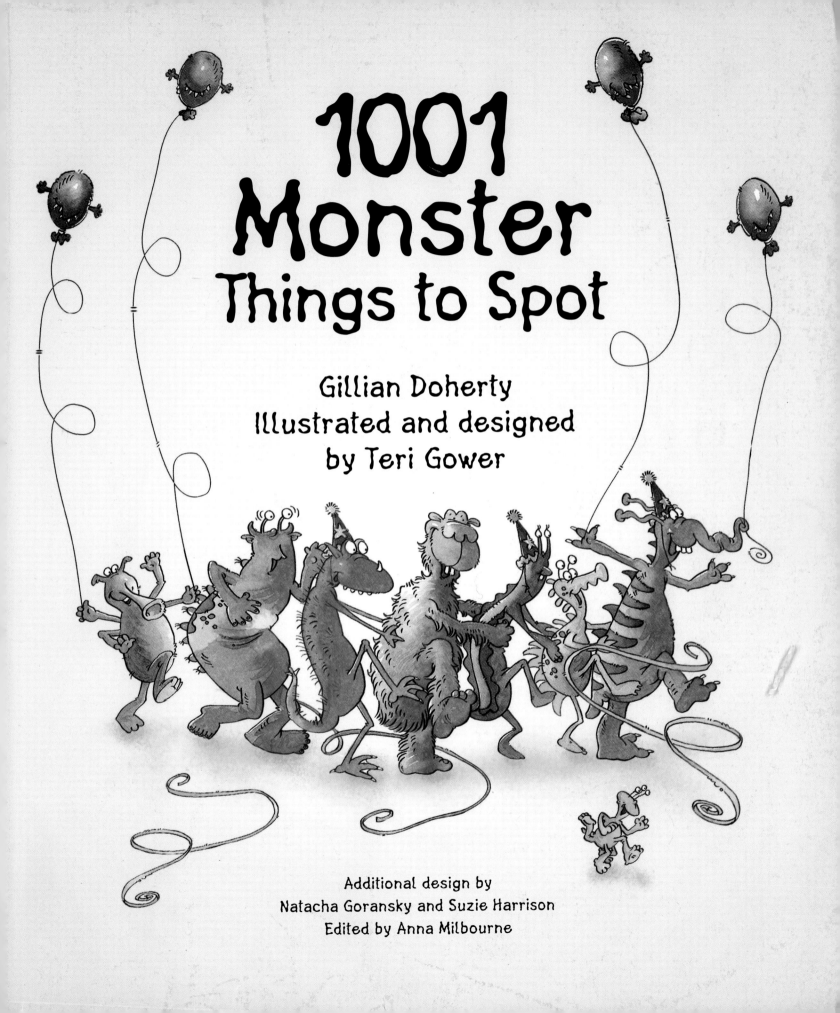

1001 Monster Things to Spot

Gillian Doherty
Illustrated and designed
by Teri Gower

Additional design by
Natacha Goransky and Suzie Harrison
Edited by Anna Milbourne

Contents

Things to Spot

Monsters come in all shapes and sizes. Most of them are very friendly, as you'll find out when you explore their monster world.

In each scene there are all kinds of monstrosities for you to find and count. There are 1001 things to spot altogether.

Monster Party

5 clodhoppers 6 trombugles 8 wowows 9 party hats 1 monstrous cake

8 monster poppers 10 monster balloons 9 boogaloos 6 striped presents 4 humdingers

28

29

Each little picture shows you what to look for in the big picture.

The number tells you how many of that thing you need to find.

Billy is crazy about monsters and when he grows up he wants to be a monsterologist. Can you find him tracking monsters in every scene?

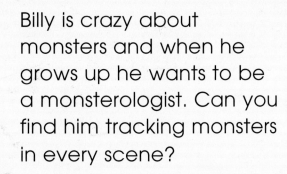

Bedroom Monsters

7 clambermanders

5 astro monsters

7 slumber busters

6 pingles

8 bubble beasts

5 pocket trolls

10 sock eaters

3 toy rockets

6 doodle monsters

9 scufflebumps

7

Midnight Feast

7 nibblers

10 scoffits

9 monster muffins

8 gobblitos

4 bottles of monsterade

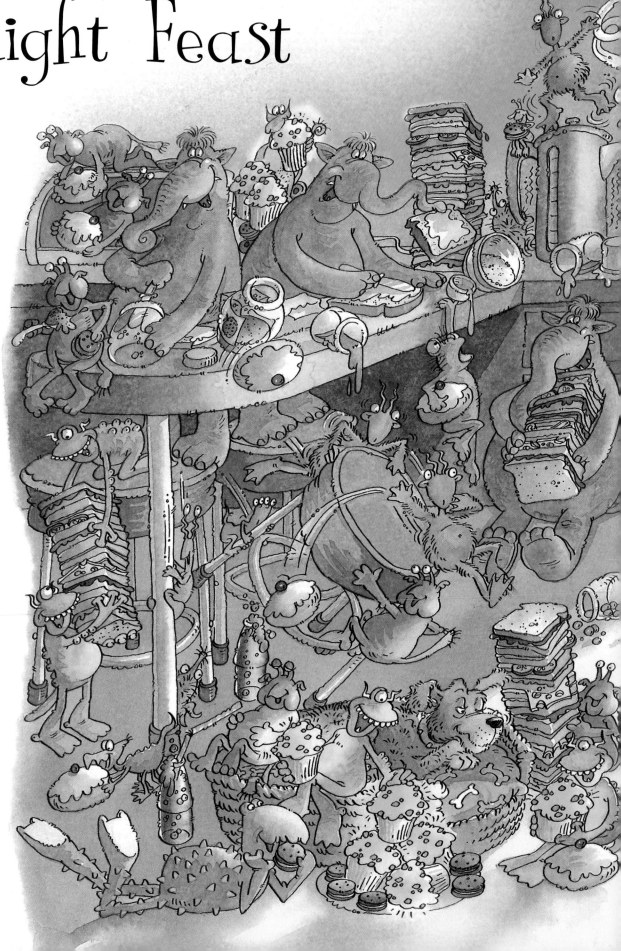

3 bellyphants

10 sticky buns

9 pot-bellied flimbos

6 chomps

5 towering sandwiches

Monster Nursery

10 roaring rattles   **5** toddling sproggles   **9** toy monsters   **7** fuzzy grizzles   **6** mollycoddles

2 monster mobiles

10 jigsaw pieces

3 naughty ninkles

5 diddums with messy bibs

7 monster storybooks

Freaky Market

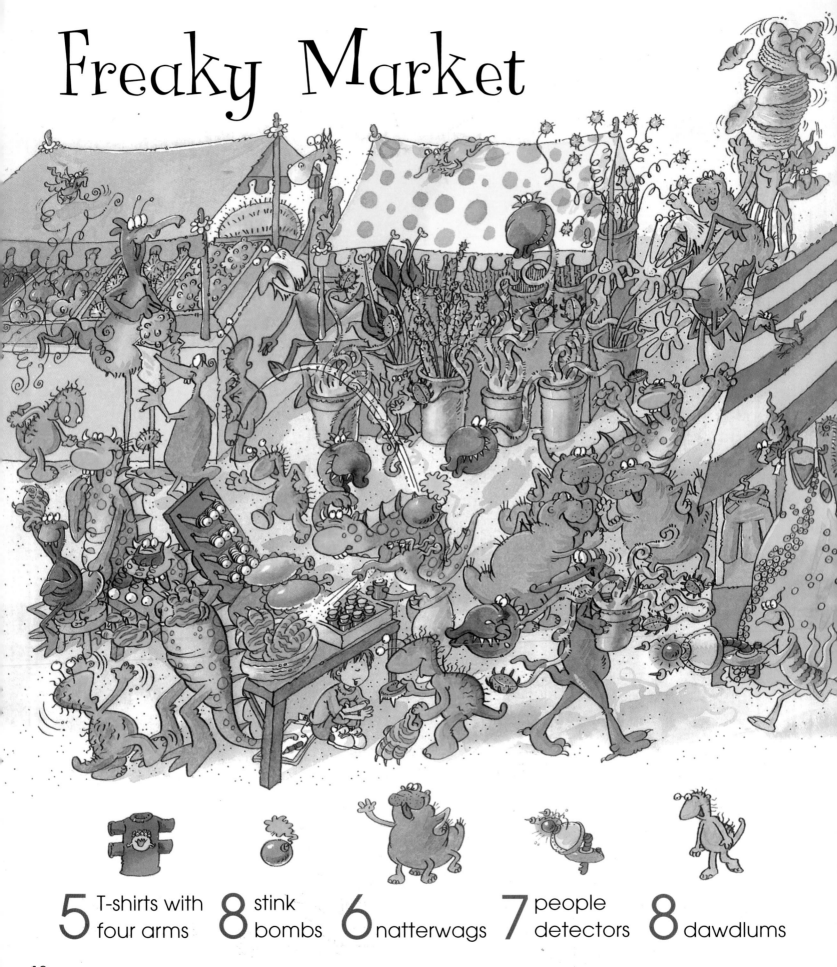

5 T-shirts with four arms **8** stink bombs **6** natterwags **7** people detectors **8** dawdlums

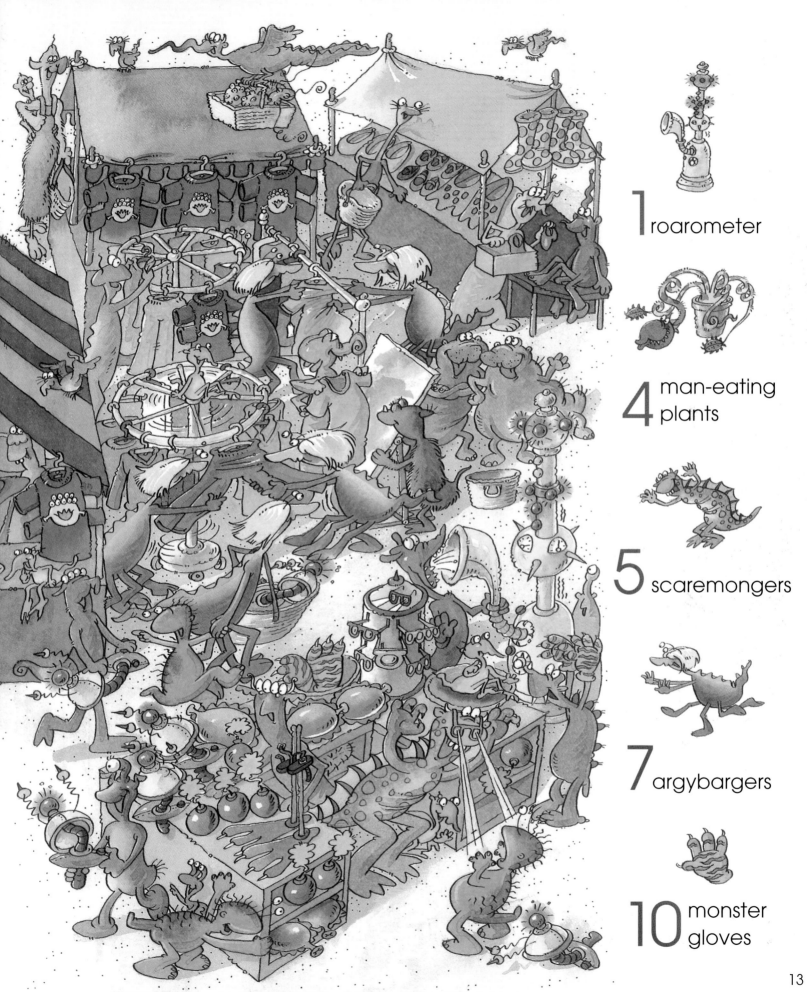

1 roarometer

4 man-eating plants

5 scaremongers

7 argybargers

10 monster gloves

Monster Park

5 monster kites

10 beastballers

1 monster cycle

2 three-headed dogs

7 boingy beasts

10 fuzzy frisbees 9 hopadoos 6 zoobers skating 3 quimbles on swings 5 hurlyburbles

15

Beastly School

4 misfangles

6 yellow munchboxes

8 swotty blots

9 school ties

7 one-eyed gumps

5 polkadot backpacks

7 scamps

9 paper planes

10 pen porters

6 quagvarks

Creepy Camp

7 snugglebugs
9 giant spiders
8 owligators
1 campfire
10 spooky lanterns

6 hairy howlers

3 growling guitars

10 monstrous shadows

9 buzzwings

8 shufflesnaps

Beach Beasts

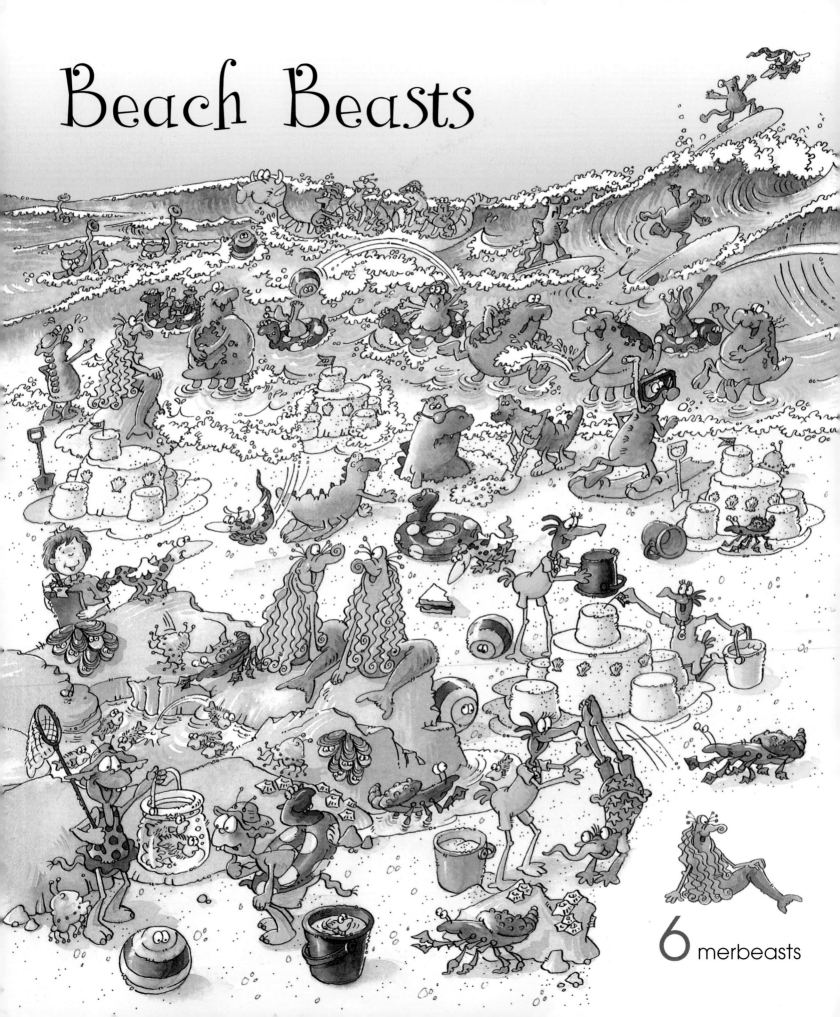

6 merbeasts

10 rubber rings

6 giant sandcastles

9 craggles

8 beach balls

8 bobsurfers

10 furry fish

7 bloops

9 wingles

2 sea squibbles

Carnival Parade

1 huffalump

 **10** monster masks

 **1** carnival queen

 5 humungous drums

 **8** razzle dazzles

 7 feather headdresses

 10 flower garlands

 **4** juggling jombles

 **8** jingles

 **6** sambasauruses

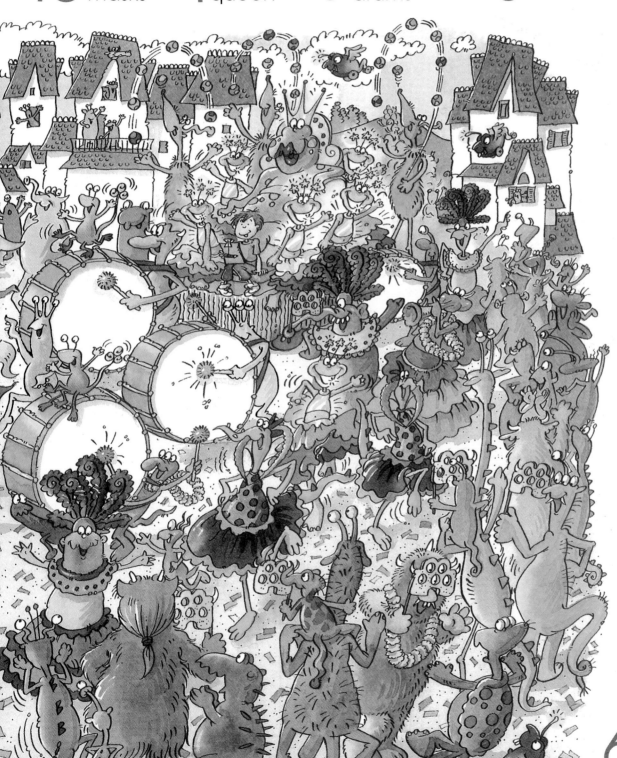

Monster Hospital

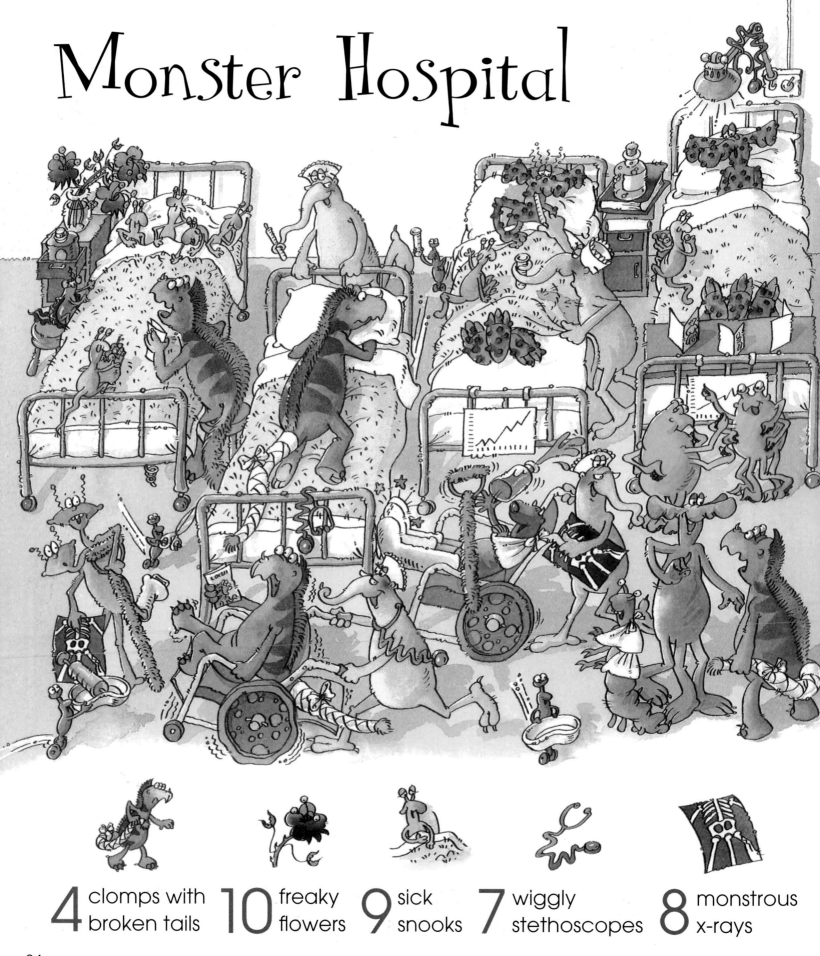

4 clomps with broken tails 10 freaky flowers 9 sick snooks 7 wiggly stethoscopes 8 monstrous x-rays

10 pootles 4 octodoctors 8 noddle nurses 5 wuffles with lumpitis 9 furry crutches

Beauty Salon

8 powder puffs

5 beasticians

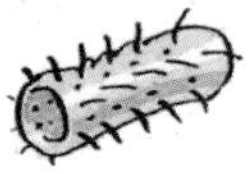

9 yellow rollers

10 bottles of claw varnish

7 ugly mugglies

9 pink bows 4 monster furdryers 10 snippets 7 bigwigs 8 splendiferoos

Monster Party

5 clodhoppers 6 trombugles 8 wowows 9 party hats 1 monstrous cake

8 monster poppers 10 monster balloons 9 boogaloos 6 striped presents 4 humdingers

29

Snow Monsters

10 huge footprints

5 yetis

8 skidoobles

9 frostbiters

3 ice giants

10 snowballs

6 snow buggies

7 snozzlebird ski lifts

4 snow monsters

9 pairs of earmuffs

Monster Gallery

Not all monsters are big and bold. Some are shy and tricky to spot. Billy's pictures of some of these bashful beasts are on show at the monster gallery. Can you find them hiding in the monster scenes?

7 hushabillies

10 shadow huggers

6 phobies

8 skulks

9 heebie jeebies

6 dweebles

8 bashflubbers

10 jitterbugs

9 grimples

5 blushums

9 wheedles

7 peekaboos

8 quivers

Answers

Did you find all the shy monsters from the monster gallery? Here's where they are:

10 shadow huggers
Bedroom Monsters
(pages 6–7)

6 phobies
Freaky Market
(pages 12–13)

8 skulks
Midnight Feast
(pages 8–9)

7 hushabillies
Monster Hospital
(pages 24–25)

9 heebie jeebies
Creepy Camp
(pages 18–19)

6 dweebles
Beastly School
(pages 16–17)

8 bashflubbers
Monster Park
(pages 14–15)

10 jitterbugs
Monster Party
(pages 28–29)

9 grimples
Snow Monsters
(pages 30–31)

5 blushums
Beauty Salon
(pages 26–27)

9 wheedles
Carnival Parade
(pages 22–23)

7 peekaboos
Monster Nursery
(pages 10–11)

8 quivers
Beach Beasts
(pages 20–21)

1001 Wizard Things to Spot

Gillian Doherty

Illustrated by Teri Gower

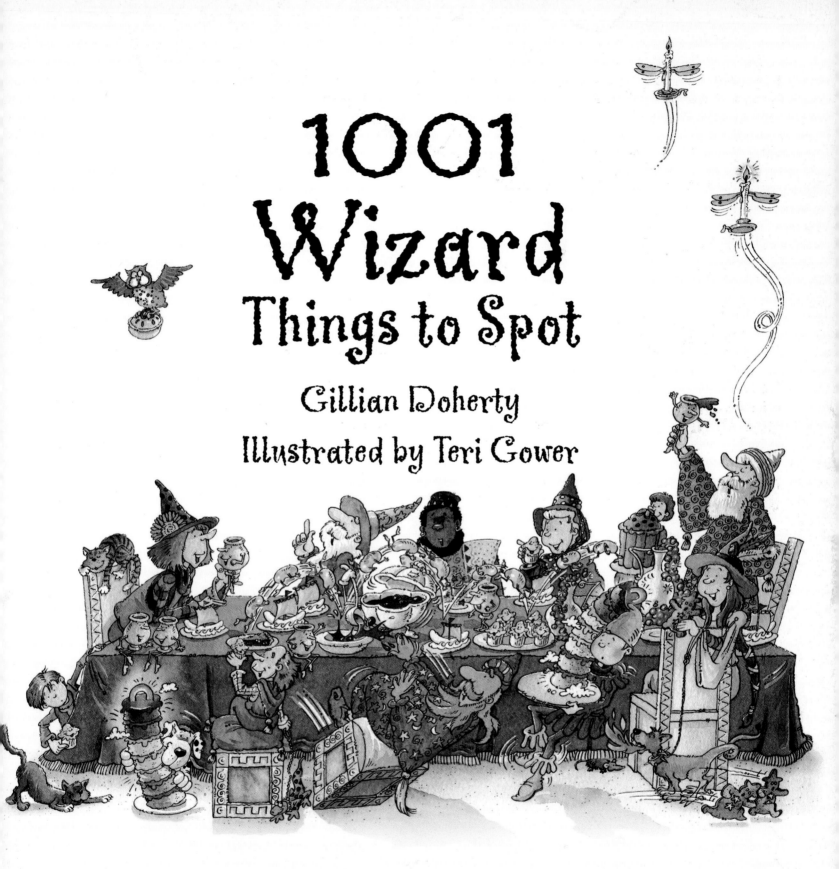

Designed by Teri Gower and Helen Wood

Edited by Anna Milbourne

Contents

Things to Spot

Welcome to the magical world of wizards, where nothing is quite what it seems. In each scene there are all kinds of extraordinary things for you to find and count. There are 1001 things to spot altogether.

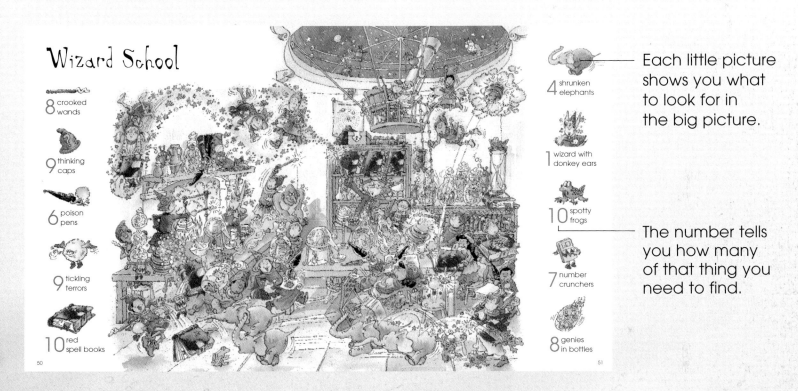

Wizard School

8 crooked wands

9 thinking caps

6 poison pens

9 tickling terrors

10 red spell books

50

51

4 shrunken elephants

1 wizard with donkey ears

10 spotty frogs

7 number crunchers

8 genies in bottles

Each little picture shows you what to look for in the big picture.

The number tells you how many of that thing you need to find.

Pip is a wizard's assistant. He's trying to learn all about magic, but it's not as easy as it looks. Can you find him in every scene?

Wizard's Castle

5 snappy crocodiles

6 dragons

7 hippogriffs

4 turrets with gold roofs

3 chimeras

9 troll guards

10 gargoyles

8 dream clouds

2 griffins

1 welcoming wizard

39

Secret Library

2 walkabout ladders

10 flying books

9 book pixies

4 wizards snoozing

1 grandfather clock

40

Meteorology

Botany

10 bookworms   7 ghosts   9 quill pens   8 spell scrolls   6 hedgehog paperweights

Curious Kitchen

10 runaway spoons

1 whistling kettle

5 cookbooks

7 busy brooms

9 soot imps

8 brownies

7 hungry mice

1 black cat

6 flame sprites

8 chocolate charm cakes

43

Wizards' Feast

9 spooky soufflés

10 flying candles

4 pumpkin pies

7 rainbow cakes

6 gingerbread wizards

8 magic muffins

9 talking goblets

10 jumping jellybeans

5 jugs of fizzy pop

7 banana boats

Magic Shop

7 sneaky spyglasses

8 flying boots

9 jars of dragons' teeth

6 warty toads

5 turbo broomsticks

8 bottles of beauty potion

9 crystal balls

5 purple wizard hats

10 love charms

7 star wands

Magic Garden

7 fairies

9 mandrake plants

6 magic watering cans

8 snapdragons

9 venus flytraps

10 garden gnomes

7 money trees

1 wishing well

10 runner beans

2 firebirds

Wizard School

8 crooked wands

9 thinking caps

6 poison pens

9 tickling terrors

10 red spell books

4 shrunken elephants

1 wizard with donkey ears

10 spotted frogs

7 number crunchers

8 genies in bottles

Midsummer Fair

5 wizards in bumper cars

 **7** carousel horses

 **8** cuddly dragons

 **10** hoop snakes

 **9** hydra heads

 **1** bouncy castle

 **10** juggling balls

 **4** roperites

 **9** rubberadoes

 **10** swirly lollipops

Enchanted Forest

1 unicorn   **8** forest elves   **9** will-o'-the-wisps   **7** grumpy dwarfs   **4** trees with faces

10 moon blooms **9** toadstools **8** star flowers **10** tree sprites **5** silver sickles

Treasure Cave

1 guard dragon

8 emerald rings

6 dwarfs with wheelbarrows

9 hobgoblins

10 gold bars

6 gold diggers

9 ruby necklaces

6 swords

8 treasure chests

7 stone serpents

Wizards' Battle

10 pixie pirates

8 shrieking squalls

7 sand boggles

9 brave starfish

5 seaweed monsters

1 spellbound octopus

7 cowardly crabs

8 sea wizards

6 sea dragons

9 shell boats

Wizard Games

 **9** dragons' eggs

 **6** whirling wibblers

 **2** silver whistles

 **8** gold medals

 **10** magic arrows

 **9** witches on broomsticks

 **8** hullabaloos

 **1** wizard on springs

 **10** fairy cheerleaders

Halloween Parade

10 pumpkin lanterns

9 vampire bats

4 mummies

5 green ghouls

3 wizards in starry robes

9 naughty imps

7 skeletons

6 purple monsters

5 owls flying

6 spooky spirits

The Great Escape

Pip has forgotten to lock the stable doors and his master's magical beasts have escaped. Can you help him find them? They are hidden throughout the wizard scenes.

10 water leapers

10 basilisks

7 centaurs

6 mugwumps

6 swagglers

8 squonks

9 gobblegonks

4 fauns

5 yetis

10 tripoderoos

6 werewolves

7 spriggans

9 burble boffins

Answers

Did you help Pip find all the magical beasts?
Here's where they are:

10 water leapers
Wizard's Castle
(pages 38–39)

10 basilisks
Magic Garden
(pages 48–49)

7 centaurs
Enchanted Forest
(pages 54–55)

6 mugwumps
Curious Kitchen
(pages 42–43)

6 swagglers
Wizards' Battle
(pages 58–59)

8 squonks
Magic Shop
(pages 46–47)

9 gobblegonks
Wizards' Feast
(pages 44–45)

4 fauns
Secret Library
(pages 40–41)

5 yetis
Wizard Games
(pages 60–61)

10 tripoderoos
Midsummer Fair
(pages 52–53)

6 werewolves
Halloween Parade
(pages 62–63)

7 spriggans
Treasure Cave
(pages 56–57)

9 burble boffins
Wizard School
(pages 50–51)

1001
Things to Spot
in
Fairyland

Gillian Doherty
Illustrated by Teri Gower

Designed by Teri Gower and Doriana Berkovic
Edited by Anna Milbourne

Contents

Things to spot

Fairyland is a magical place where just about anything can happen, and often does. Each of these scenes has all kinds of wonderful and surprising things for you to find and count. There are 1001 things to spot altogether.

Fairy palace

10 stripy fish

7 spotty turtles

10 pink flags

8 mermaids

7 boats with leaf sails

8 nutshell boats

10 fairy horses

9 elf archers

6 pearls

8 goblin guards

Each little picture shows you what to look for in the big picture.

The pink number tells you how many of that thing you need to find.

Dizzy Rainbow is new in fairyland and is busy exploring and discovering its secrets. Can you find her in every scene?

Fairy feast

10 leaf trays

9 bowls of marshmallows

10 sugar mice

9 blackberry tarts

8 yellow bows

7 paper garlands

10 strawberry drinks

9 fairy cakes

1 greedy goblin

8 plates of star cookies

Enchanted waterfall

10 rainbow fish

8 yellow frogs

5 fairies in hammocks

9 flying fish

10 emeralds

2 kingfishers

3 fairies washing their hair

5 mirrors

7 treasure chests

6 elves diving for jewels

Moon dance

7 shooting stars

10 white rabbits

6 pixies on toadstools

1 full moon

9 fairies with sparkly wings

10 fairy lanterns

2 snowy owls

8 glow-worms

1 unicorn

2 golden slippers

Fairy school

7 fairies having flying lessons

6 writing quills

10 purple beetles

3 pumpkin coaches

8 spell books

10 magic wands

9 white mice

5 frog princes

1 baby dragon

8 pink snails

Magic market

10 jars of fairy kisses

9 candy canes

7 petal parasols

8 magic lamps

7 rainbow cauldrons

8 spell scrolls **4** flying carpets **10** book worms **9** wizard hats **10** boxes of wishes

Secret garden

6 pink flower fairies

 **10** dandelion clocks

 **4** fairies splashing

 **9** dragonflies

 **5** daisy chains

 **9** yellow butterflies

 8 stripy caterpillars

 **10** bluebells

 **7** yellow flower fairies

 **8** elves riding snails

Fairy palace

 **10** stripy fish

 **7** spotty turtles

 10 pink flags

 **8** mermaids

 **7** boats with leaf sails

8 nutshell boats **10** fairy horses **9** elf archers **6** pearls **8** goblin guards

House fairies

8 stripy socks

6 spotty socks

10 pink buttons

1 sleepy cat

10 spools of thread

9 blue pins

7 fairies sewing

9 star buttons

5 fairies bouncing

7 cobweb dresses

Rainbow fairies

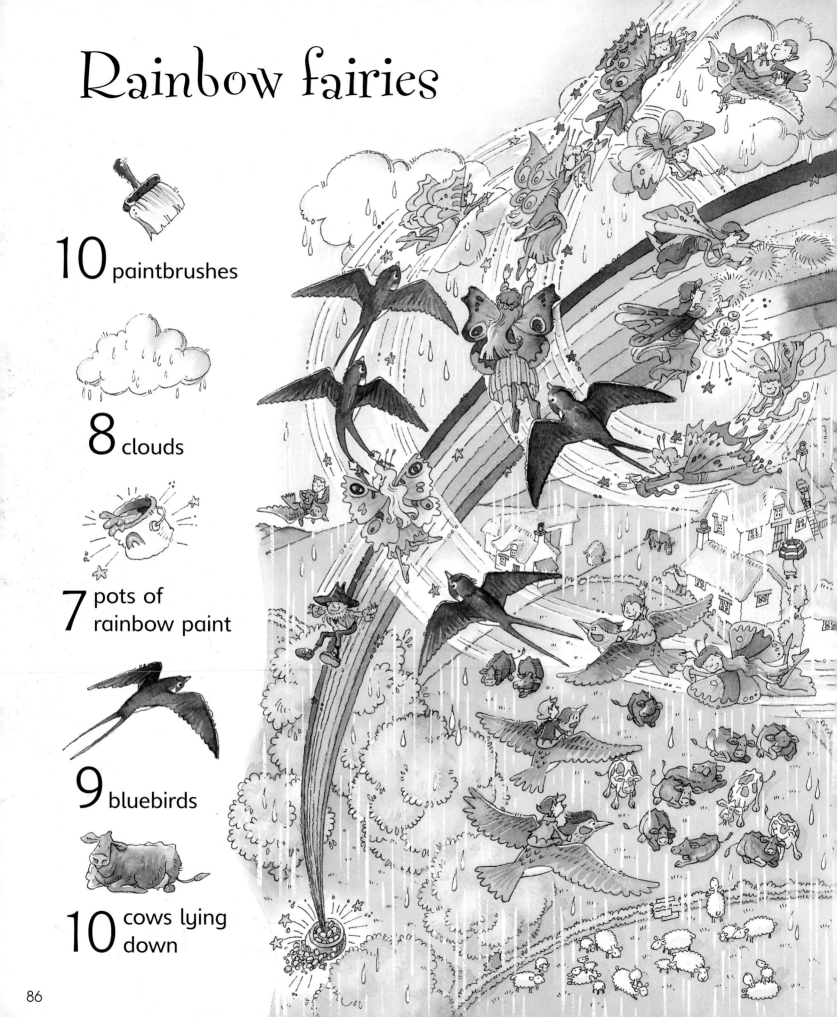

10 paintbrushes

8 clouds

7 pots of rainbow paint

9 bluebirds

10 cows lying down

1 leprechaun

8 stripy umbrellas

9 pixies riding on skylarks

1 pot of gold

10 chimney pots

Treetop fairies

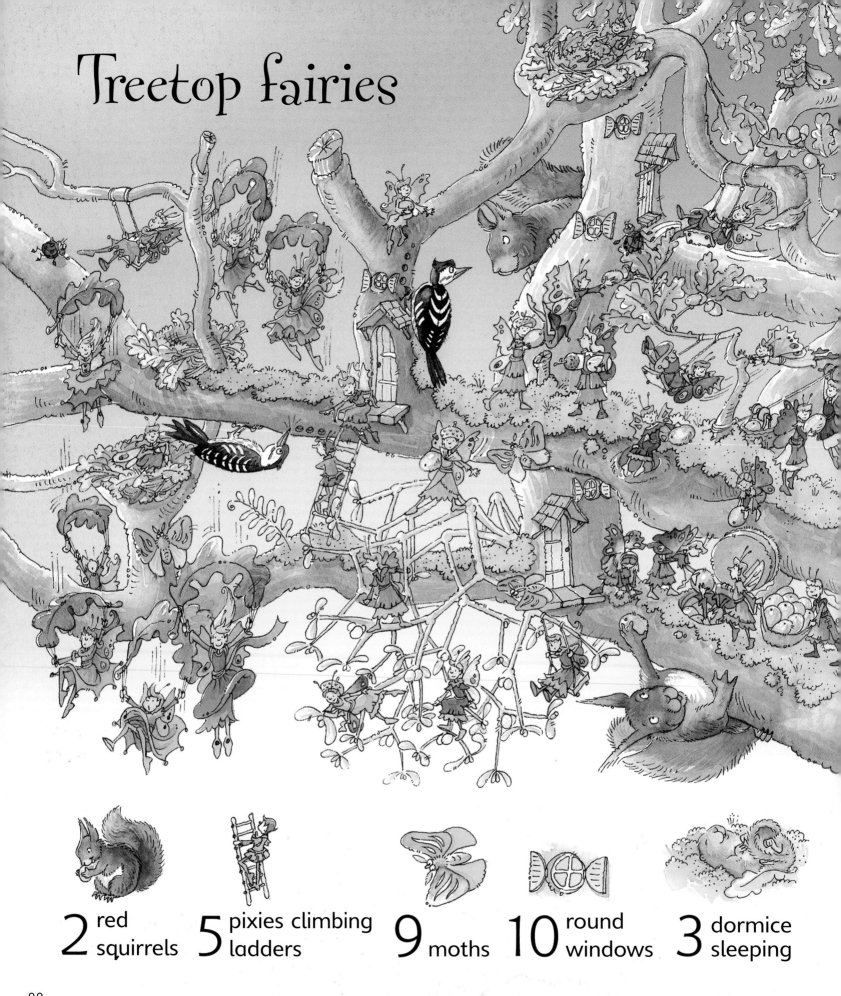

2 red squirrels

5 pixies climbing ladders

9 moths

10 round windows

3 dormice sleeping

3 woodpeckers

6 fairies on swings

9 treehouse doorways

10 fairies with acorn hats

8 leaf parachutes

Fairy treehouse

9 candles

7 marbles

3 fairy newspapers

9 building blocks

8 feather dusters

 6 baby fairies

 **4** self-flipping pancakes

 **1** pink rabbit

 10 flyaway letters

 2 snow fairies

Fairyland workshop

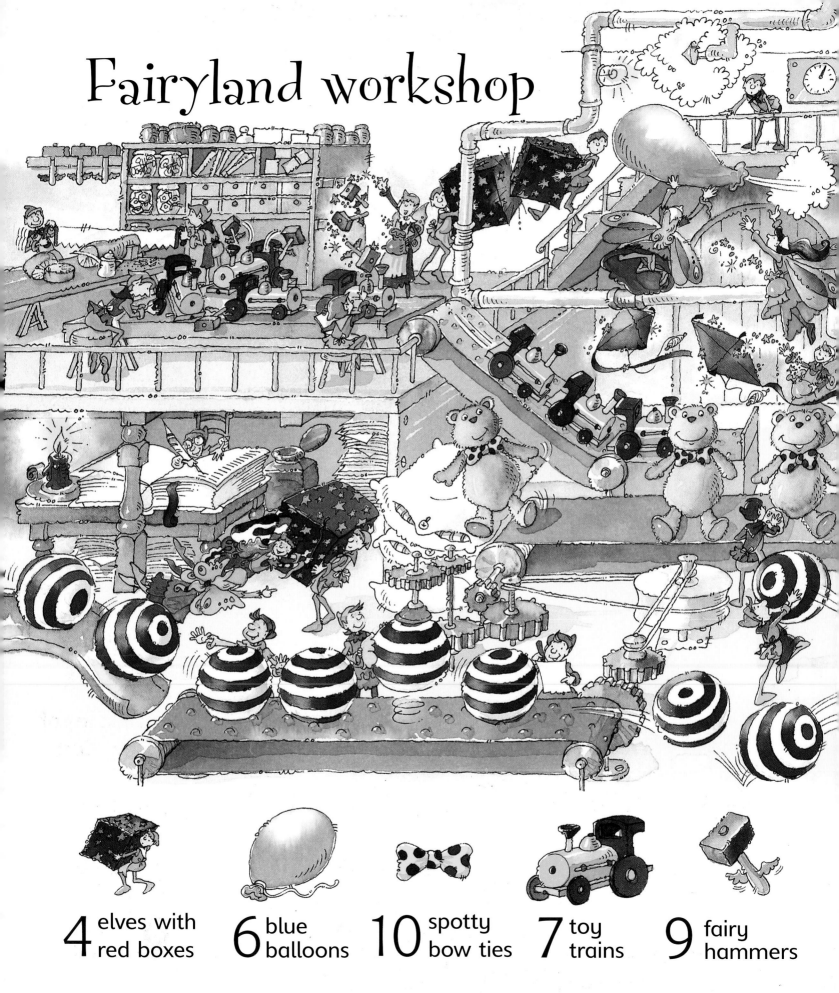

4 elves with red boxes

6 blue balloons

10 spotty bow ties

7 toy trains

9 fairy hammers

10 stripy balls

1 jack-in-a-box

3 fairies pulling levers

7 pouches of fairy dust

8 teddy bears

The Snow Queen's ball

7 fairies with fluffy hats

3 ice thrones

9 goblets of fairy punch

10 snowballs

3 golden crowns

94

2 golden
bowls

8 red
mittens

10 fairies
ice-skating

1 crystal
chandelier

7 snow hares

Dizzy Rainbow's magic spells

Dizzy Rainbow is just about to start fairy school.
She needs all kinds of strange things for her magic
class. Look back through the fairyland scenes and
see if you can help her find them all.

9 bottles of magic potion

10 bird footprints

3 rubies

2 kites

1 ice harp

9 pots of honey

10 bats

9 foxgloves

2 toads

10 buckets of raindrops

4 spiders

5 birds' nests

10 magic arrows

Answers

Did you find all the things Dizzy Rainbow needs for her magic class? Here's where they are:

9 bottles of magic potion:
Magic market
(pages 78–79)

10 bird footprints:
Fairy treehouse
(pages 90–91)

3 rubies:
Enchanted waterfall
(pages 72–73)

2 kites:
Fairyland workshop
(pages 92–93)

1 ice harp:
The Snow Queen's ball
(pages 94–95)

9 pots of honey:
Fairy feast
(pages 70–71)

10 bats:
Moon dance
(pages 74–75)

9 foxgloves:
Secret garden
(pages 80–81)

2 toads:
Fairy school
(pages 76–77)

10 buckets of raindrops:
Rainbow fairies
(pages 86–87)

4 spiders:
House fairies
(pages 84–85)

5 birds' nests:
Treetop fairies
(pages 88–89)

10 magic arrows:
Fairy palace
(pages 82–83)

1001 Pirate
Things to Spot

Rob Lloyd Jones

Illustrated by Teri Gower

Designed by Teri Gower and Michelle Lawrence
Edited by Anna Milbourne
Digital manipulation by Nick Wakeford

Contents

Things to spot

These pirates are a lively bunch of scurvy sea dogs. They love fighting, partying and searching for buried treasure. Each pirate scene has all kinds of exciting things for you to find and count. There are 1001 things to spot altogether.

Pirate port

6 anchors   5 carthorses   9 baskets of fish   5 parrots in cages   10 Jolly Rogers   3 pirates with peg legs   9 pieces of eight   10 barrels of gunpowder   8 stray dogs   5 pelicans

110   111

Each little picture shows you what to look for in the big picture.

The blue number tells you how many of that thing you need to find.

This is Jack, the cabin boy on the pirate ship. He's always busy doing all the pirates' hard work. See if you can spot him in each scene, and then help him with his treasure hunt on page 128.

Life at sea

1 pirate captain

10 striped T-shirts

7 mops

4 telescopes

5 purple pirate hats

9 rats

7 sacks of grain

10 scrawny chickens

3 ship's cats

5 pirates on
the rigging

The captain's feast

10 ships in bottles   9 mice   7 bowls of stew   6 pineapples   8 chicken legs

 **5** pirates with eye patches

 9 lanterns

 **10** cups of punch

 **5** fat cats

 **3** pirates in hammocks

Attack!

10 cutlasses

7 tied-up prisoners

5 fist fights

10 flintlocks

8 blunderbusses

106

4 men walking the plank

6 parrots shrieking

9 grappling hooks

8 cannons

9 cannonballs

Keeping shipshape

5 saws   10 spotted lizards   7 dice   4 pirates sewing sails   8 ladders

10 woodworms

5 buckets of tar

9 hammers

7 scrubbing brushes

3 campfires

Pirate port

6 anchors

5 carthorses

9 baskets of fish

5 parrots in cages

10 Jolly Rogers

3 pirates with peg legs
9 pieces of eight
10 barrels of gunpowder
8 stray dogs
5 pelicans

Pirate school

10 pirate school books

7 pirate teachers

6 yellow ropes

7 training boats

5 baby parrots

8 wooden cutlasses

4 training cannons

3 sea charts

10 quills

8 catapults

Pirate races

4 pirates water-skiing

6 turtles

4 pirates diving

10 pirate armbands

9 seagulls

7 dolphins

2 surfboards

8 blue pairs of shorts

1 finishing flag

114

10 seaweed
pom-poms

Treasure island

4 treasure maps 6 toucans 8 coconuts 9 monkeys 10 shovels

2 castaways 7 pickaxes 9 crabs 10 iguanas 1 X-marks-the-spot

Pirate party

10 pirate party hats

4 barrels rolling

3 fiddles

9 flower garlands

5 monkeys dancing

9 plates of party cakes

7 chinese lanterns

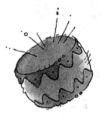
6 drums

8 lollipops

10 pirate balloons

Monsters of the deep

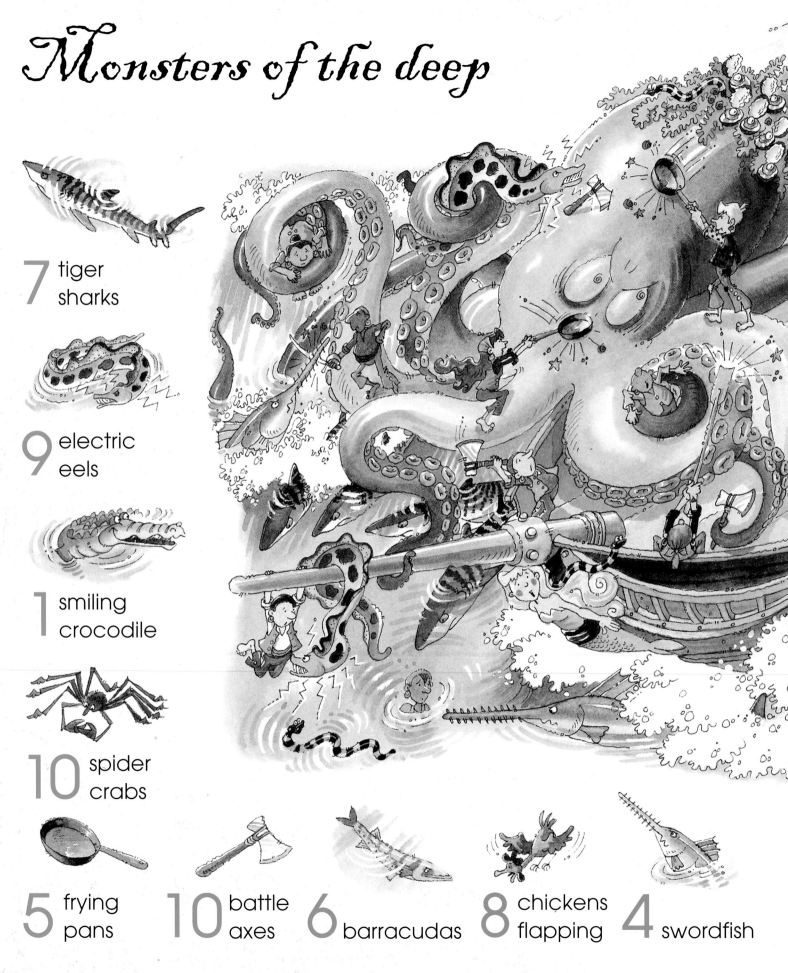

7 tiger sharks

9 electric eels

1 smiling crocodile

10 spider crabs

5 frying pans

10 battle axes

6 barracudas

8 chickens flapping

4 swordfish

120

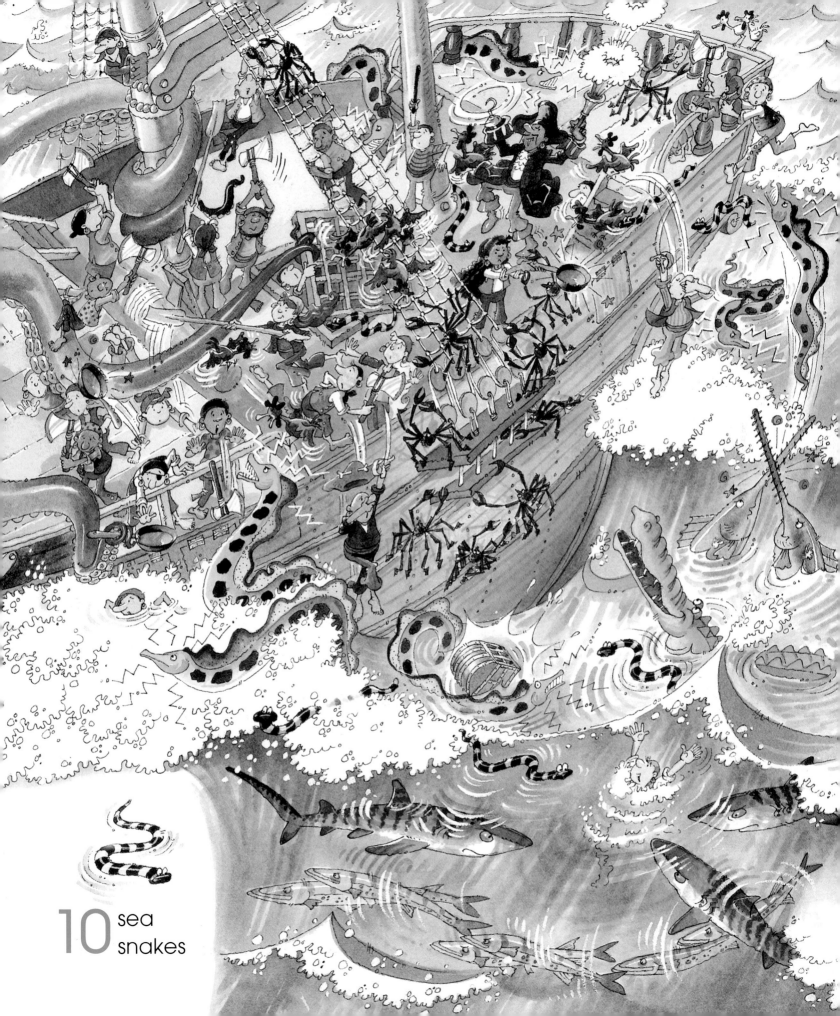

10 sea
snakes

Ghost ship

9 skeleton pirates

4 mummies

9 pirate ghosts

5 pirates trembling

6 vultures

122

9 vampire bats

10 giant cobwebs

8 scary spiders

3 creepy coffins

6 vampire rats

Stormy sea

10 men overboard

5 buckets

4 bolts of lightning

8 life rings

5 pirate umbrellas

5 seasick pirates

8 shark fins

9 barrels floating

1 lighthouse

10 pirates in raincoats

125

Shipwreck

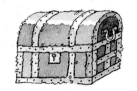

1 treasure chest

4 octopuses

7 broken cannons

6 rusty cutlasses

10 gold doubloons

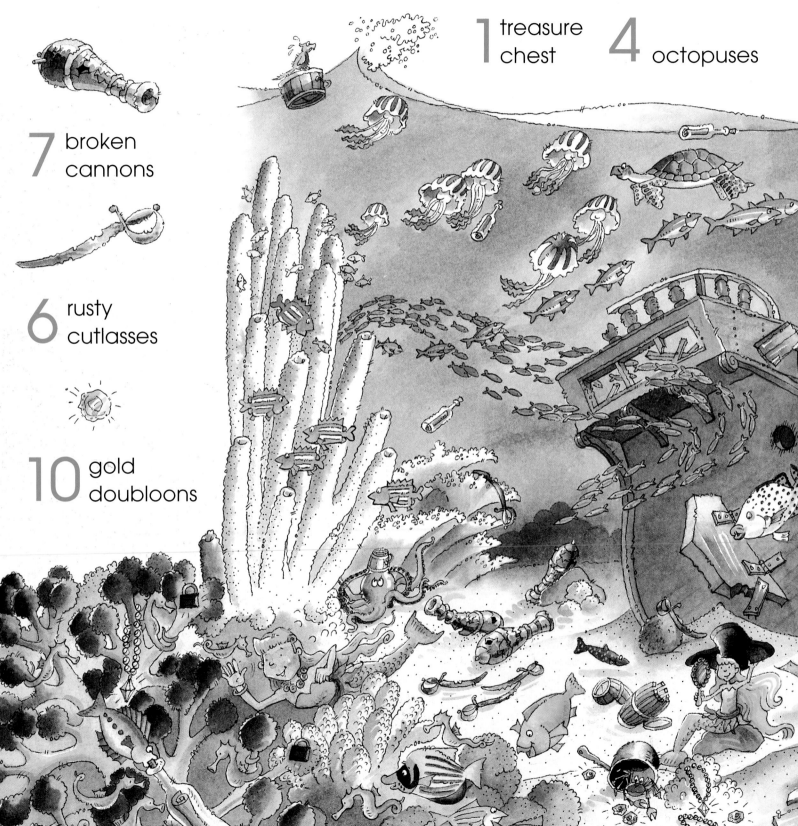

9 mermaids 10 jellyfish 8 sea horses 5 messages in bottles 7 clownfish

Treasure hunt

Jack has found a wooden chest washed up on a beach. It's packed full of glittering treasure collected by the pirates on their adventures. Look back through the pirate scenes and see if you can find and count it all.

 7 silver tankards

 10 gold bars

 9 emeralds

 5 golden compasses

 6 pearls in shells

 3 gold medals

9 silver spoons

 7 conch shells

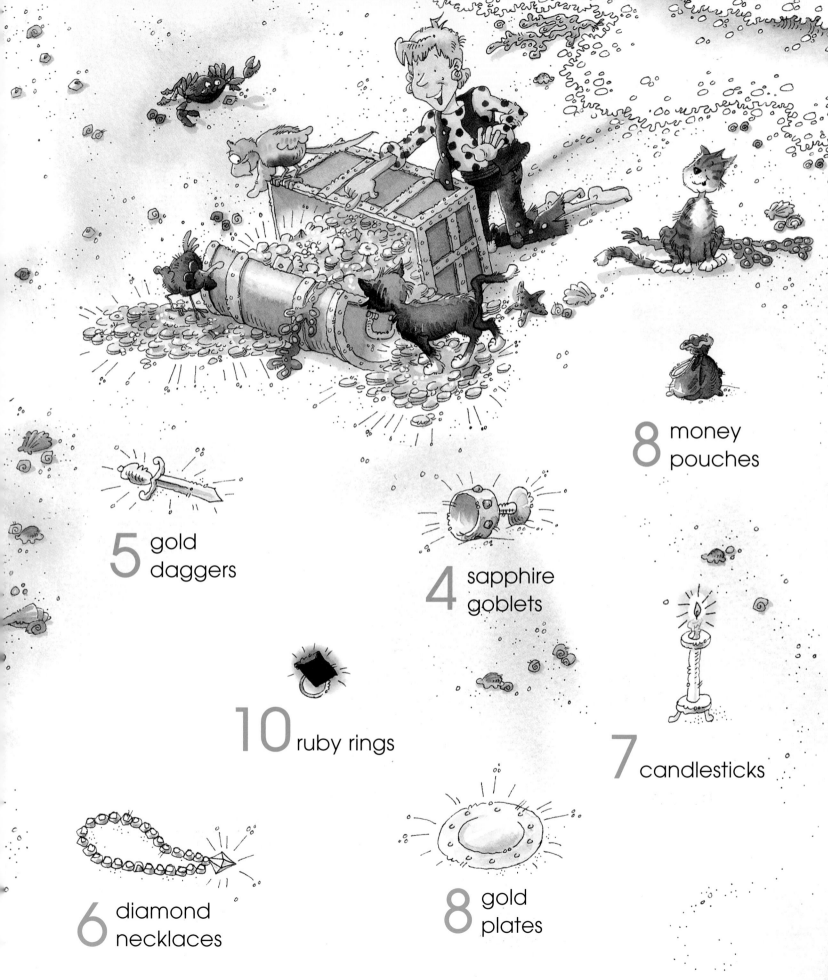

8 money pouches

5 gold daggers

4 sapphire goblets

10 ruby rings

7 candlesticks

6 diamond necklaces

8 gold plates

129

Answers

Did you spot all the treasure?
Here's where you can find it:

7 silver tankards:
The captain's feast
(pages 104-105)

9 silver spoons:
Pirate party
(pages 118-119)

10 ruby rings:
Shipwreck
(pages 126-127)

10 gold bars:
Keeping shipshape
(pages 108-109)

7 conch shells:
Treasure island
(pages 116-117)

7 candlesticks:
Ghost ship
(pages 122-123)

9 emeralds:
Stormy sea
(pages 124-125)

5 gold daggers:
Attack!
(pages 106-107)

6 diamond necklaces:
Shipwreck
(pages 126-127)

5 golden compasses:
Pirate school
(pages 112-113)

4 sapphire goblets:
Life at sea
(pages 102-103)

8 gold plates:
The captain's feast
(pages 104-105)

3 gold medals:
Pirate races
(pages 114-115)

8 money pouches:
Pirate port
(pages 110-111)

6 pearls in shells:
Monsters of the deep
(pages 120-121)

1001
Things to Spot
in the Sea

Katie Daynes

Illustrated by Teri Gower

Designed by Natacha Goransky

Edited by Anna Milbourne

Natural history consultant: Dr. Margaret Rostron

Contents

Things to spot

These scenes show seas and oceans from around the world. In each of the big pictures, there are lots of things for you to find and count.

There is also a puzzle on pages 160 to 161 with even more things to spot in the sea. There are 1001 things for you to spot altogether.

Underwater forest

Each little picture shows you what to look for in the big picture.

10 garibaldi fish

8 turban snails

5 black rock fish

9 kelp crabs

8 kelp bass

The blue number tells you how many of that thing you need to find.

4 sea otters

10 sea urchins

6 sea fans

2 leopard sharks

9 kelp fish

144

145

This is Billy. He has explored seas and oceans all over the world. He always takes his underwater camera with him. As you go through the sea pictures, see if you can spot Billy's camera in each scene.

Open sea

8 squid 10 mackerel

1 humpback
whale

10 sea
nettles

8 halfmoon
fish

3 ocean
sun fish

4 blue
sharks

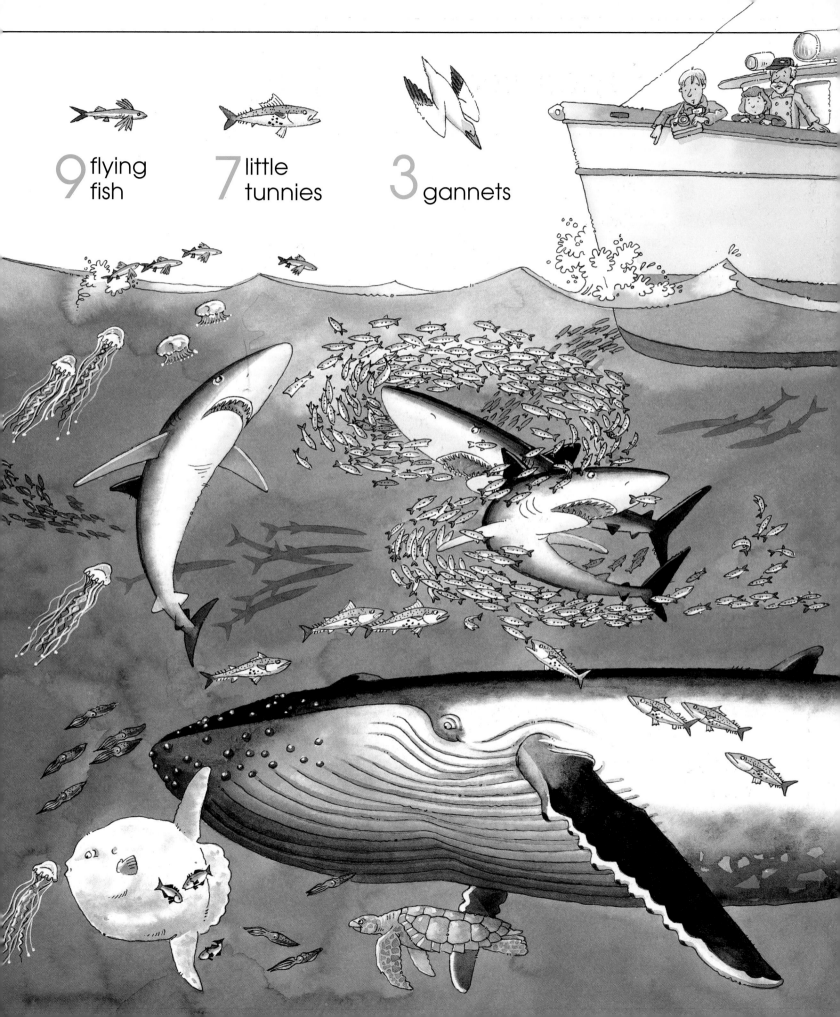

9 flying fish

7 little tunnies

3 gannets

Water sports

4 speedboats 10 flippers 5 jet skis 9 yellow life jackets 3 rubber rings

9 red buoys

6 striped sails

10 herring gulls

5 windsurfers

7 boogy boards

Icy north

10 harp seals

8 seal pups

10 capelin

4 arctic terns

8 ringed seals

4 polar bears

9 arctic cod

5 white parkas

3 killer whales

9 arctic charr

139

Coral reef

 10 anemone fish

 7 feather stars

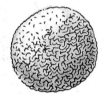 4 brain corals

 5 groupers

 6 porcupine fish

 9 dart fish

 8 sea slugs

 10 angel fish

 5 giant clams

9 trigger fish

By the seashore

7 hermit crabs

9 groups of mussels

8 oystercatchers

4 sandwiches

5 fishing nets

3 blue sunhats

10 gobies

8 shore crabs

6 black-headed gulls

8 red buckets

Underwater forest

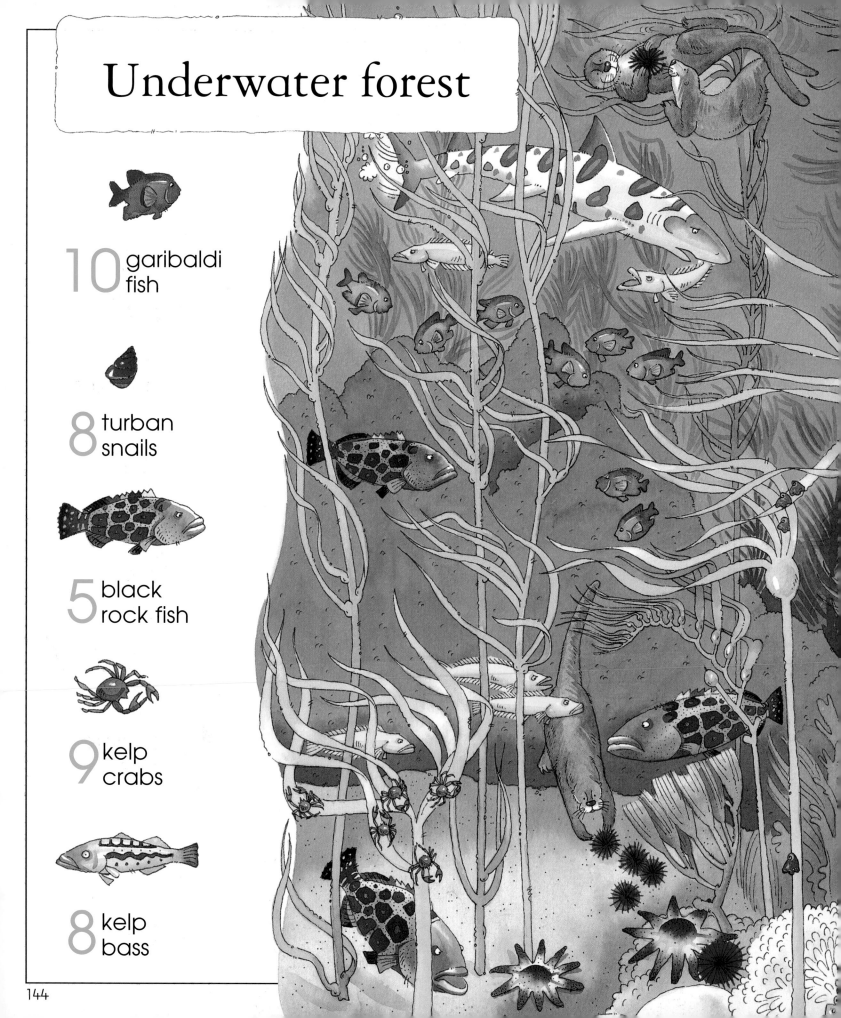

10 garibaldi fish

8 turban snails

5 black rock fish

9 kelp crabs

8 kelp bass

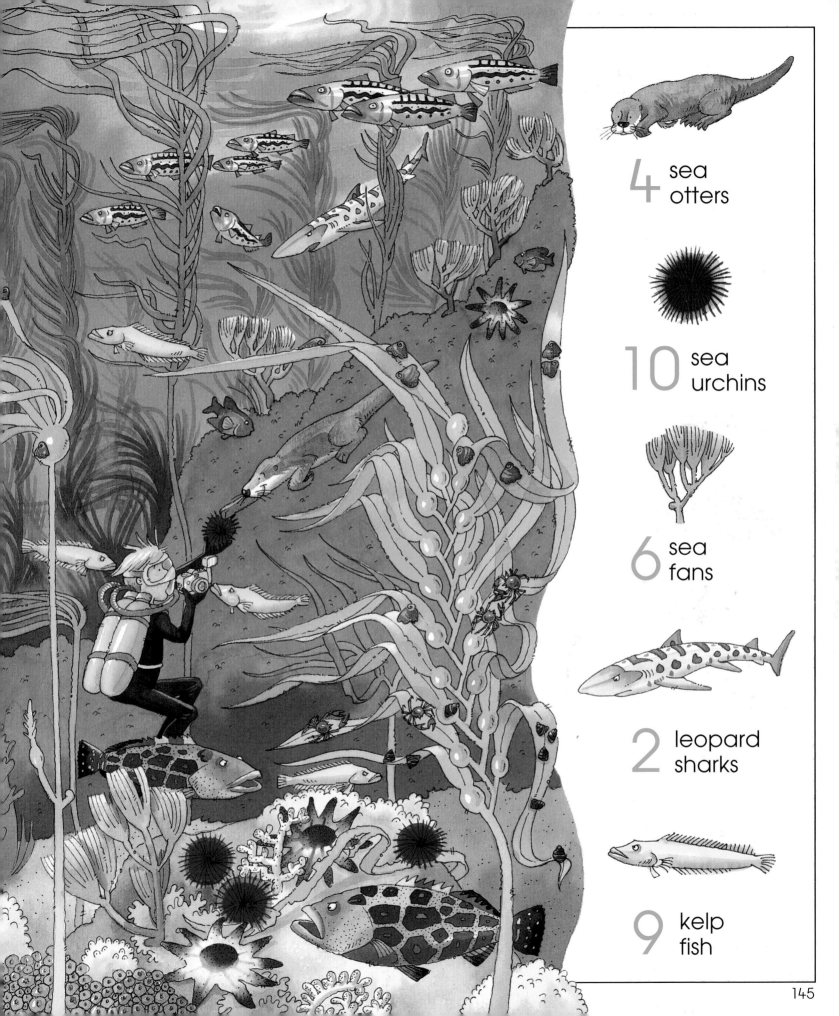

4 sea otters

10 sea urchins

6 sea fans

2 leopard sharks

9 kelp fish

On a cruise

3 lifeboats

 **7** life rings

 **8** deck lights

 **5** tables

 **4** yachts

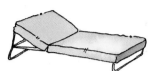 **6** yellow loungers

 **10** palm trees

 **8** striped loungers

 **9** ship's officers

 4 pairs of binoculars

Deep down

10 lantern fish

9 vent shrimps

8 spook fish

10 vent crabs

7 black smokers

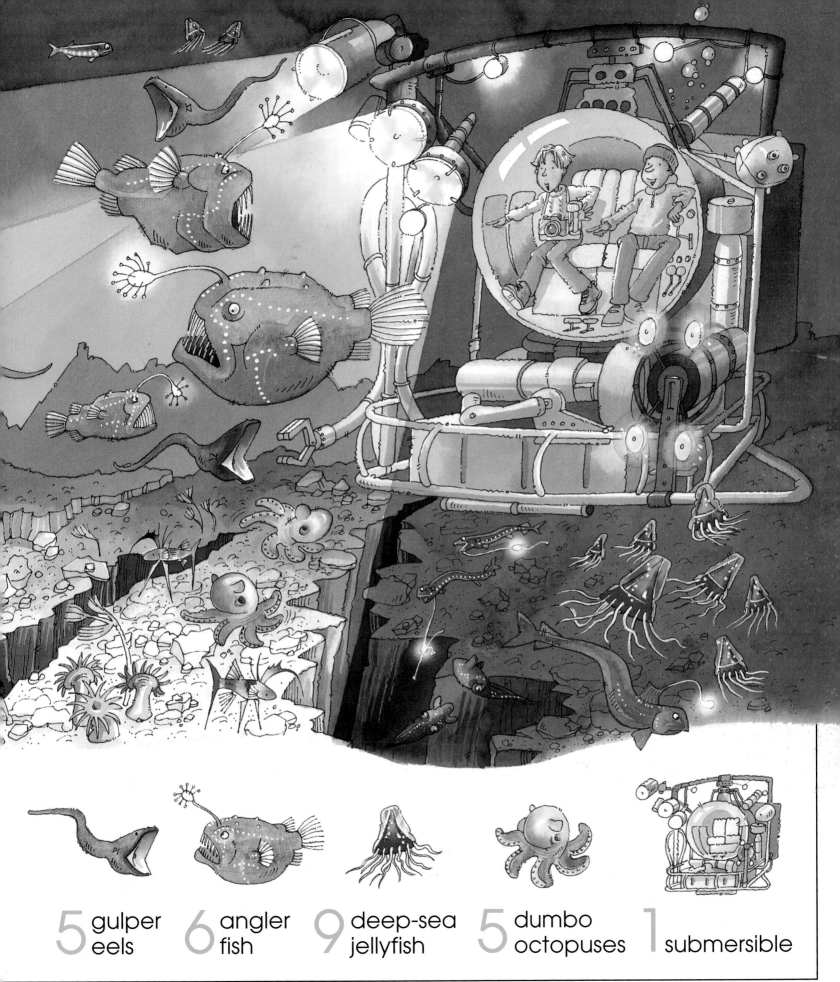

5 gulper eels 6 angler fish 9 deep-sea jellyfish 5 dumbo octopuses 1 submersible

Sea village

5 huts   9 oysters   10 durian fruits   7 canoes   5 red-footed boobies

10 paddles

8 white T-shirts

10 coconuts

6 ladders

4 dogs

Lost city

9 greeneye fish

5 jars

7 seabream

8 gold coins

10 cardinal fish

6 octopuses

9 whelk shells

10 bullet tuna

1 white stone head

7 divers

153

Chilly south

9 chinstrap penguins

8 albatrosses

1 whale-watchers' tour boat

5 elephant seals

3 whale tails
6 backpacks
10 king penguins
10 penguin chicks
9 brown skuas
4 hourglass dolphins

Grassy seabed

10 mullet

8 yellow winkles

9 catfish

3 sea cows

7 seeds

9 snappers

5 roseate spoonbills

8 blue crabs

7 terrapins

10 butterfly fish

Shipwreck

2 writing slates

9 banner fish

10 barracudas

5 carnation corals

9 squirrel fish

10 surgeon fish

7 sweetlips

4 moray eels

1 anchor

8 cow fish

At the aquarium

Aquariums help you find out about sea animals. This aquarium shows animals from the sea scenes. Can you find which pictures they are from and count them all?

7 moon jellyfish

10 emperor fish

7 bottlenose dolphins

10 walruses

3 tripod fish

10 red sea anemones

8 macaroni penguins

1 blue-spotted ray

2 napoleon wrasses

3 loggerhead turtles

8 seahorses

9 picasso fish

6 lion fish

6 spiny lobsters

7 butterfly blennies

5 sun stars

Answers

Did you find all the aquarium animals in the sea scenes? Here's where they are.

Posters of animals

7 moon jellyfish:
Open sea
(pages 134–135)

10 emperor fish:
Sea village
(pages 150–151)

7 bottlenose dolphins:
On a cruise
(pages 146–147)

10 walruses:
Icy north
(pages 138–139)

3 tripod fish:
Deep down
(pages 148–149)

10 red sea anemones:
By the seashore
(pages 142–143)

8 macaroni penguins:
Chilly south
(pages 154–155)

Animals in tanks

1 blue-spotted ray:
Shipwreck
(pages 158–159)

3 loggerhead turtles:
Open sea
(pages 134–135)

2 napoleon wrasses:
Shipwreck
(pages 158–159)

8 seahorses:
Grassy seabed
(pages 156–157)

9 picasso fish:
Coral reef
(pages 140–141)

6 lion fish:
Coral reef
(pages 140–141)

6 spiny lobsters:
Grassy seabed
(pages 156–157)

7 butterfly blennies:
Lost city
(pages 152–153)

5 sun stars:
Underwater forest
(pages 144–145)

Managing editor: Gillian Doherty
Managing designers: Mary Cartwright and Russell Punter

The publishers would like to thank the following people for their advice:

- Emad Khalil, underwater archaeologist at Southampton University
- Jonathan Mendez, chief powerboat instructor for the Royal Yachting Association
- Rachael Saul from Hebridean Island Cruises Ltd
- Matt Slater, marine biologist at Blue Reef Aquarium, Newquay
- Sally Thomas from The Royal Institute of Naval Architects

1001 Bugs to Spot

Emma Helbrough

Illustrated by Teri Gower

Designed by Natacha Goransky

Edited by Anna Milbourne

Natural history consultants:
Dr. Margaret Rostron and Dr. John Rostron

Contents

Bugs to spot

These big pictures show all kinds of places where bugs might be lurking. On every page there are lots of bugs for you to find and count. There are 1001 bugs to spot altogether. The example pages below show you what you need to do to find them all.

Each little picture shows you what to look for in the big picture.

The blue number tells you how many of that bug you need to find.

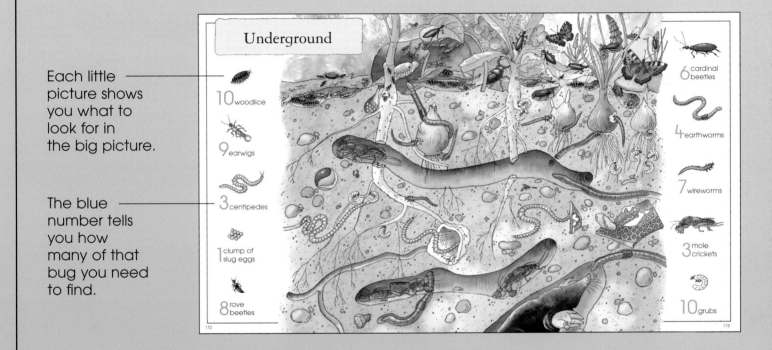

Underground

10 woodlice

9 earwigs

3 centipedes

1 clump of slug eggs

8 rove beetles

6 cardinal beetles

4 earthworms

7 wireworms

3 mole crickets

10 grubs

172

173

This is a honeybee.

Honeybees live all over the world. They collect pollen from flowers and use it to make honey. There is a honeybee flying through every big picture in this section. Can you spot them all?

There are lots more things for you to spot on pages 192 to 193.

Flowerbed

9 snails　　4 spittlebugs　　10 stink bugs　　8 pink spiders　　6 tiger moths

10 ants 3 hairy caterpillars 9 bumblebees 7 crane flies 5 peacock butterflies

Rocky desert

9 hawk wasps   **3** tarantulas

8 painted grasshoppers

4 giant centipedes

Hercules beetle image

7 Hercules beetles

5 curled-up millipedes

queen butterfly image

6 queen butterflies

168

4 hairy scorpions

10 ants with seeds

9 cactus beetles

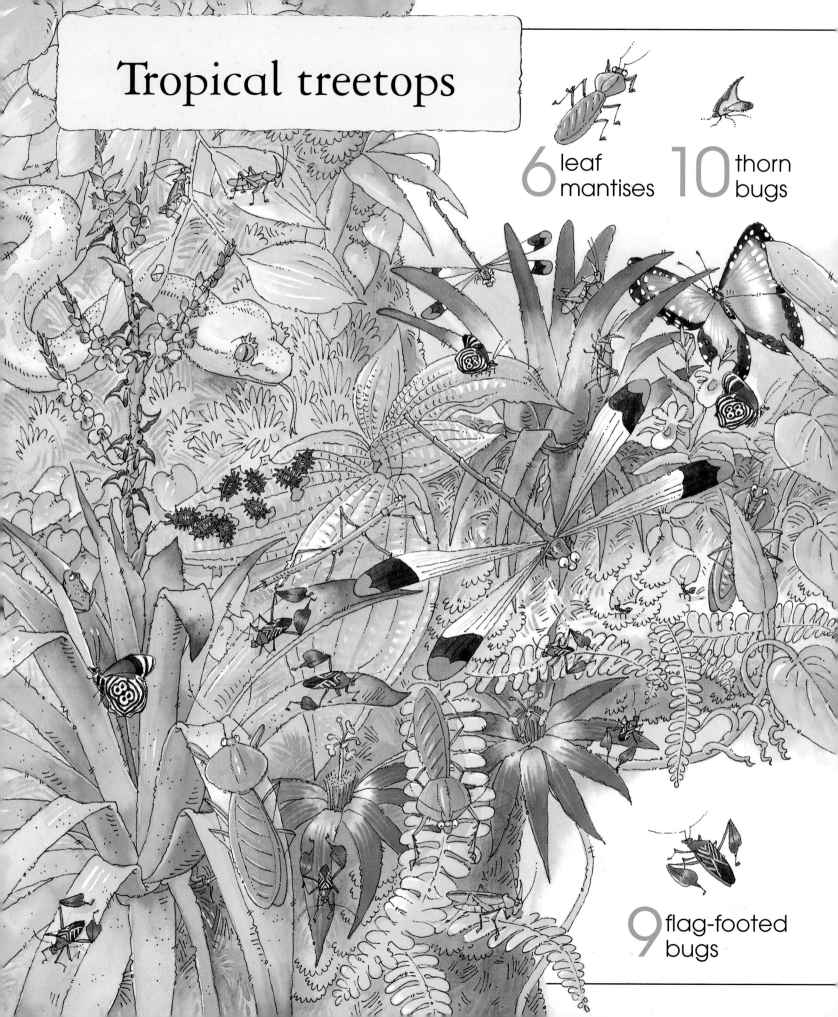

Tropical treetops

6 leaf mantises

10 thorn bugs

9 flag-footed bugs

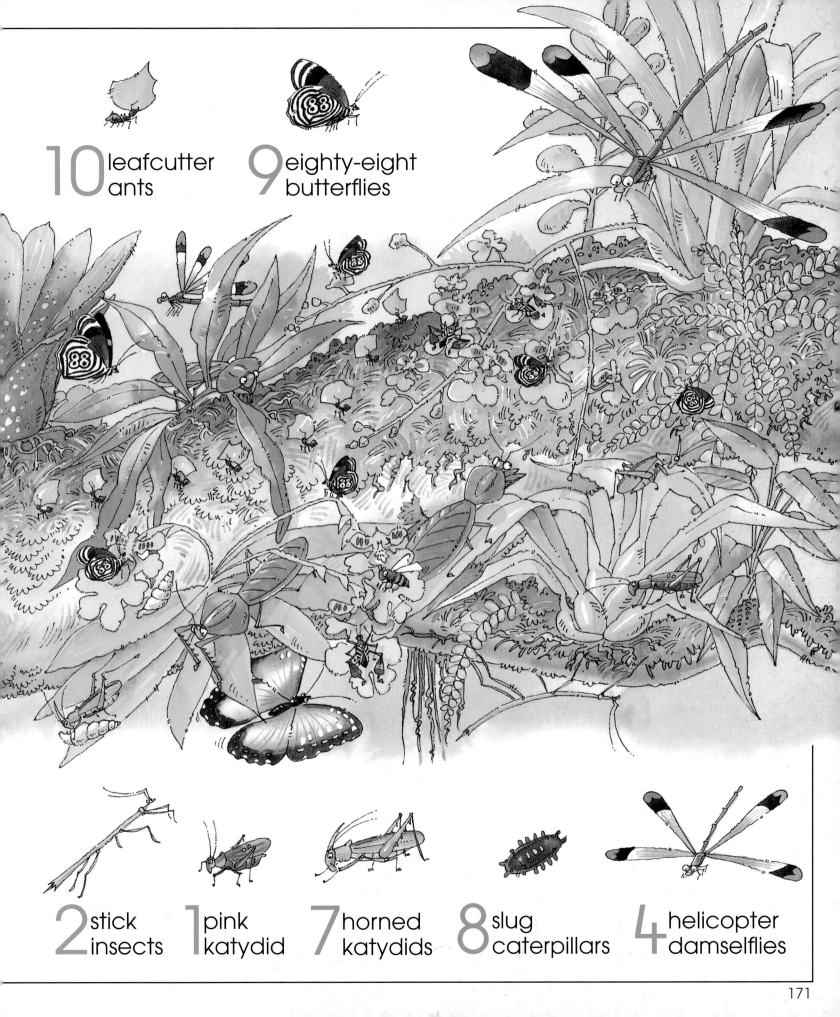

10 leafcutter ants

9 eighty-eight butterflies

2 stick insects

1 pink katydid

7 horned katydids

8 slug caterpillars

4 helicopter damselflies

Underground

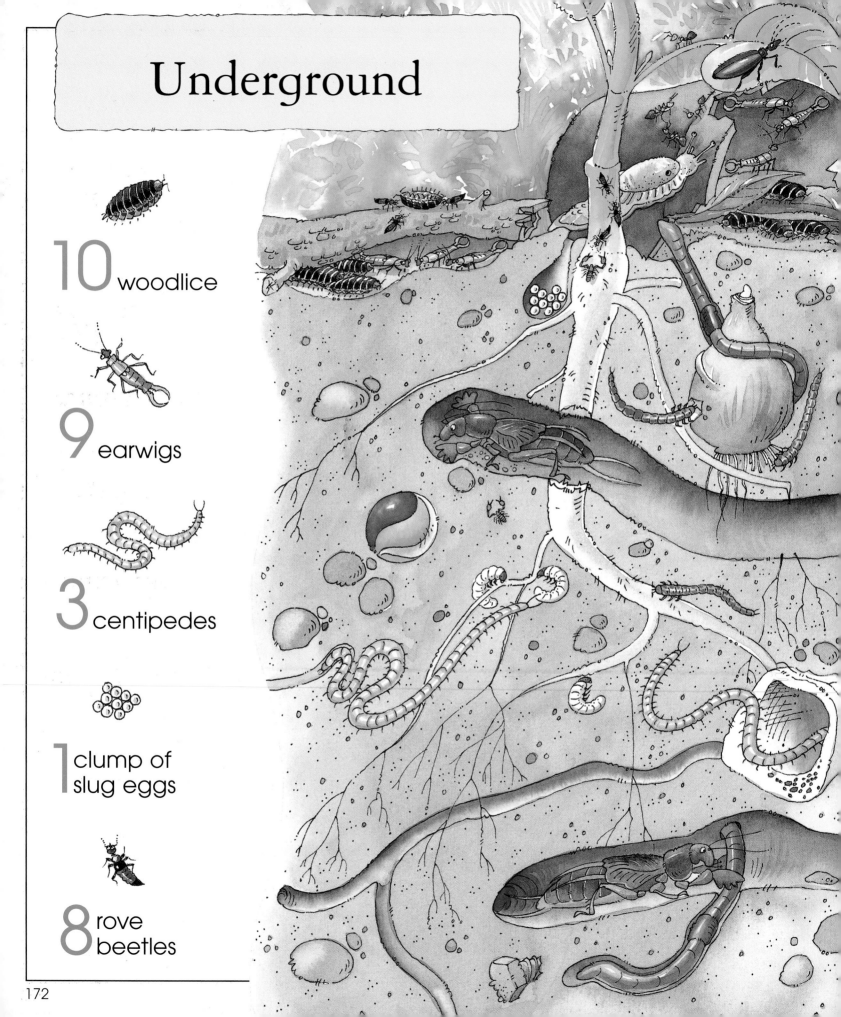

10 woodlice

9 earwigs

3 centipedes

1 clump of slug eggs

8 rove beetles

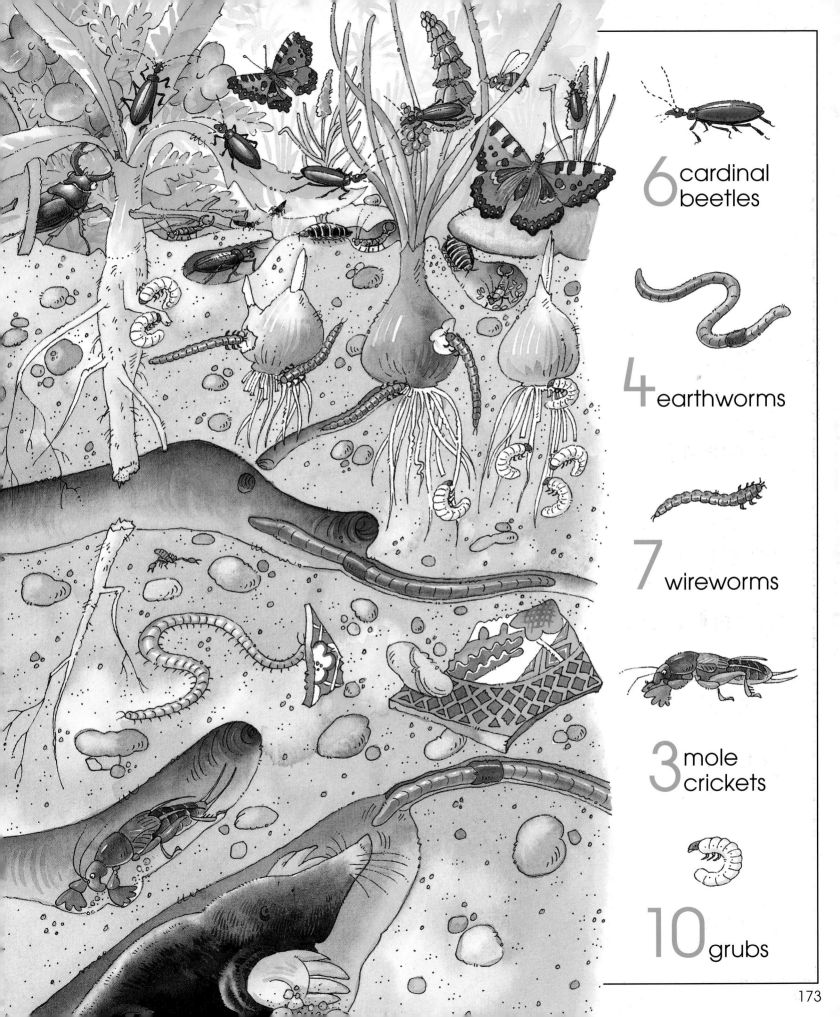

6 cardinal beetles

4 earthworms

7 wireworms

3 mole crickets

10 grubs

Sandy desert

5 painted lady butterflies

8 long-legged beetles

9 desert crickets

10 dune beetles

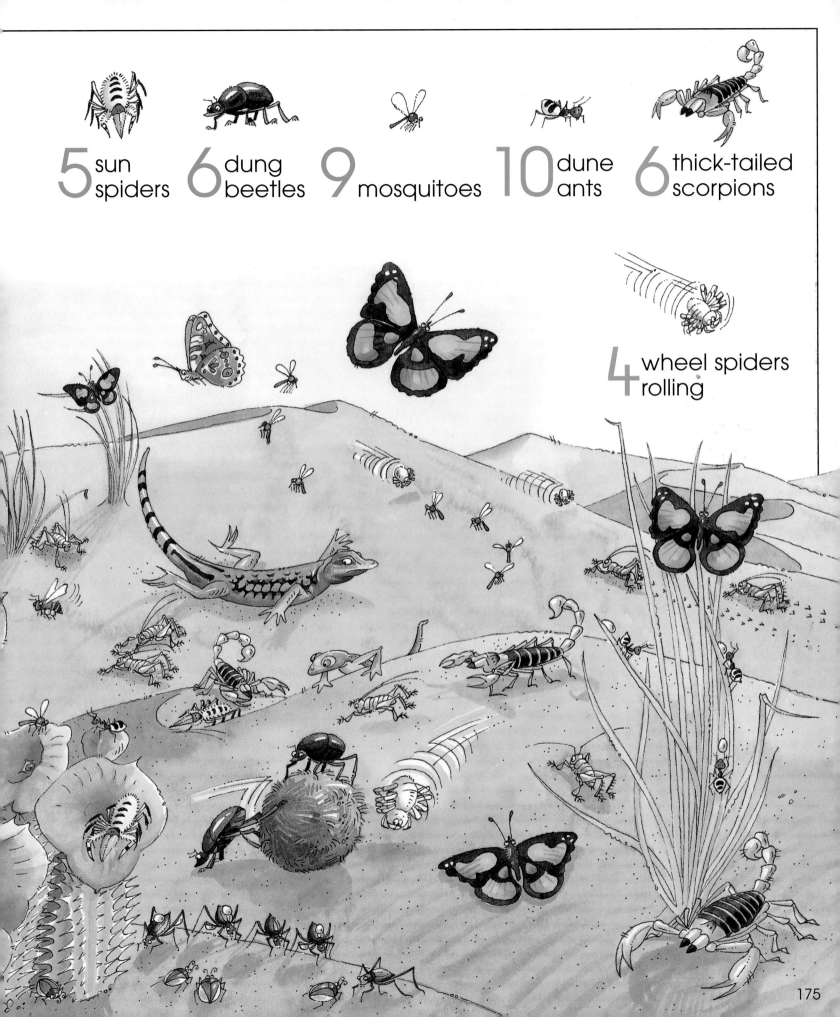

5 sun spiders

6 dung beetles

9 mosquitoes

10 dune ants

6 thick-tailed scorpions

4 wheel spiders rolling

Garden shed

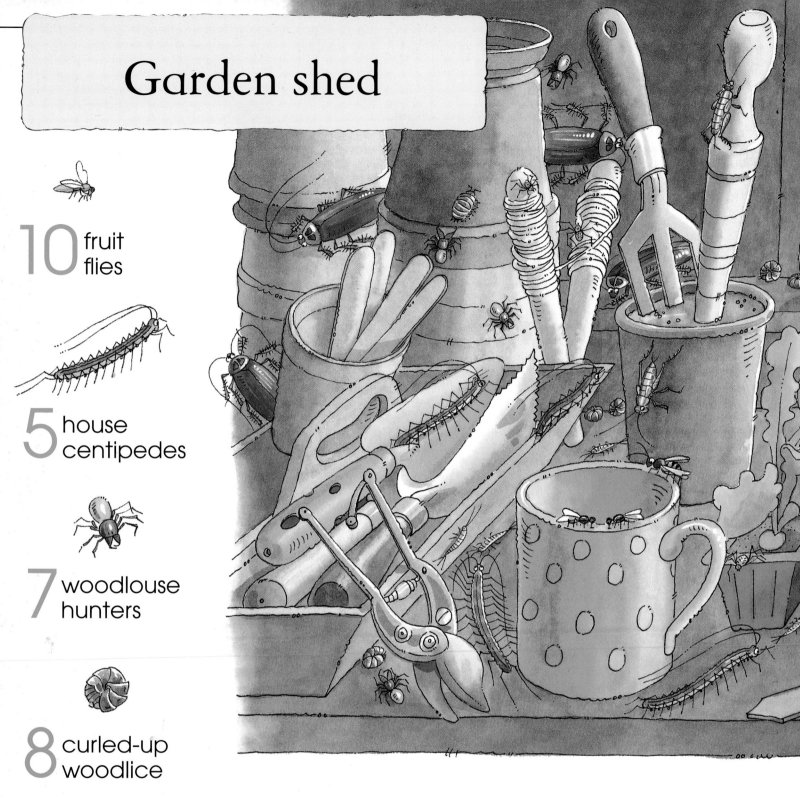

10 fruit flies

5 house centipedes

7 woodlouse hunters

8 curled-up woodlice

9 cockroaches

5 spitting spiders

10 house flies

7 silverfish

8 wasps

6 house crickets

Jungle floor

7 frog beetles　9 horned spiders　10 pill millipedes　8 longhorn beetles　2 pink dragonflies

9 yellow stink bugs

8 palm weevils

6 lantern bugs

9 stalk-eyed flies

7 harlequin butterflies

Vegetable patch

9 lacewings

3 yellow spiders

7 slugs

10 leaf hoppers

4 striped beetles

10 spotted beetles

5 buckeye butterflies

6 harlequin bugs

8 banded snails

6 looper caterpillars

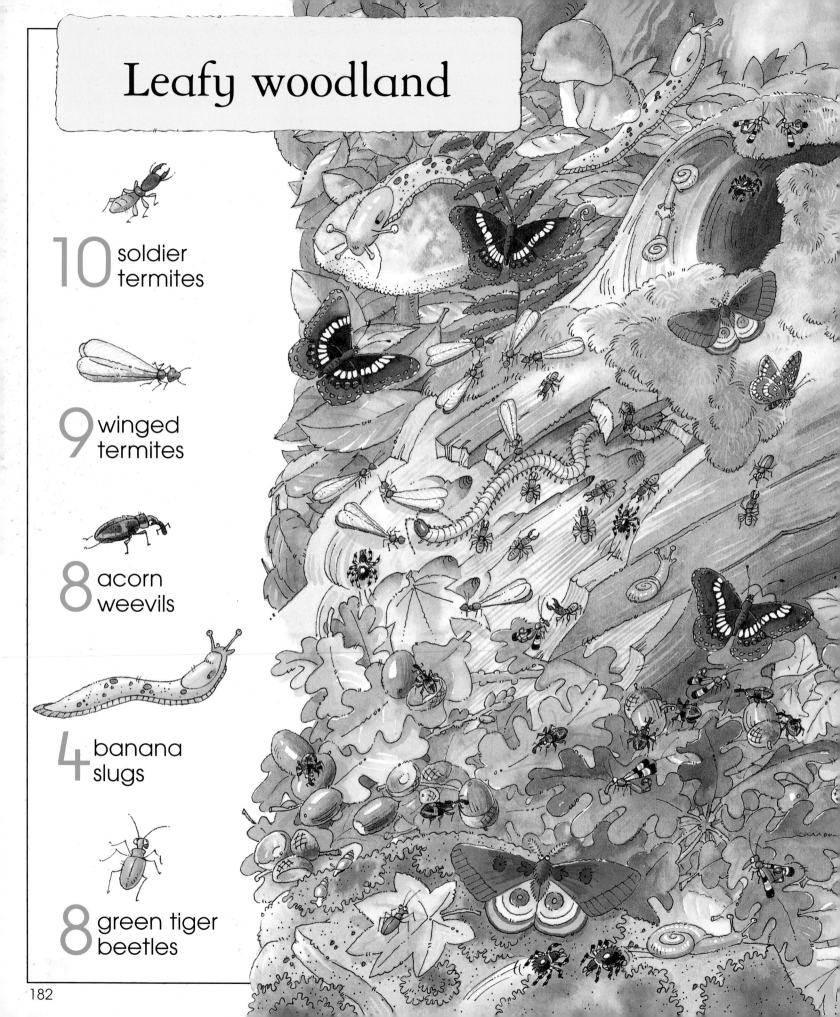

Leafy woodland

10 soldier termites

9 winged termites

8 acorn weevils

4 banana slugs

8 green tiger beetles

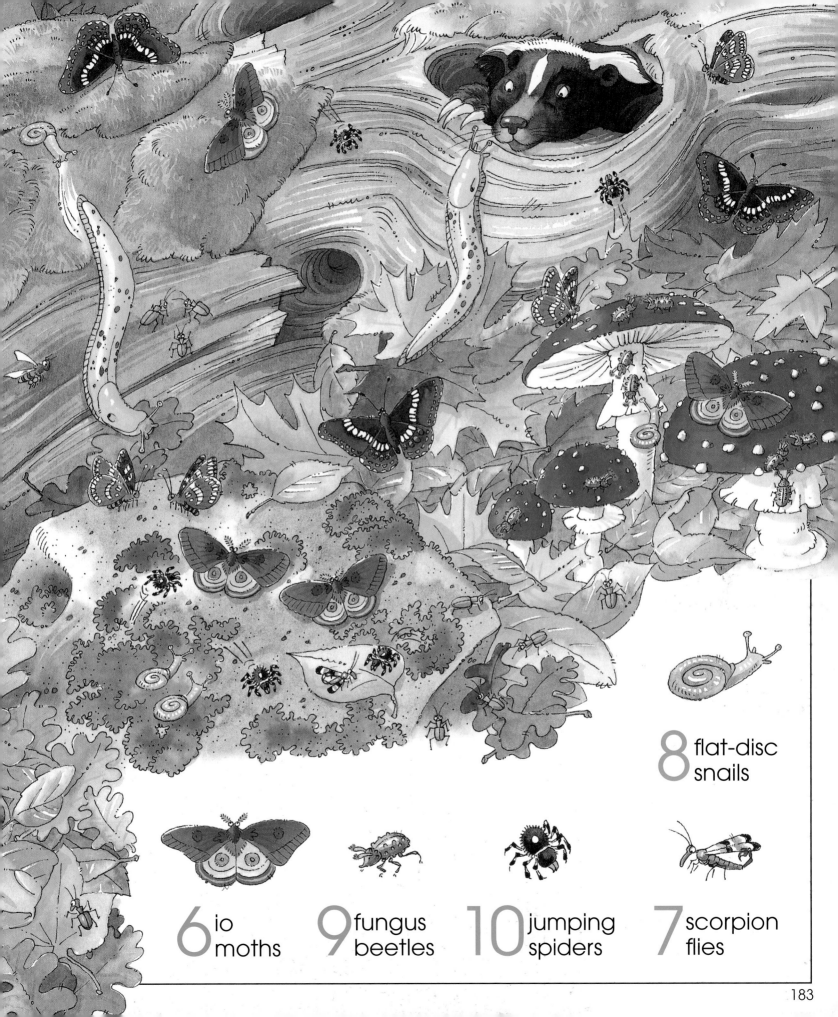

8 flat-disc
snails

6 io
moths

9 fungus
beetles

10 jumping
spiders

7 scorpion
flies

Pond life

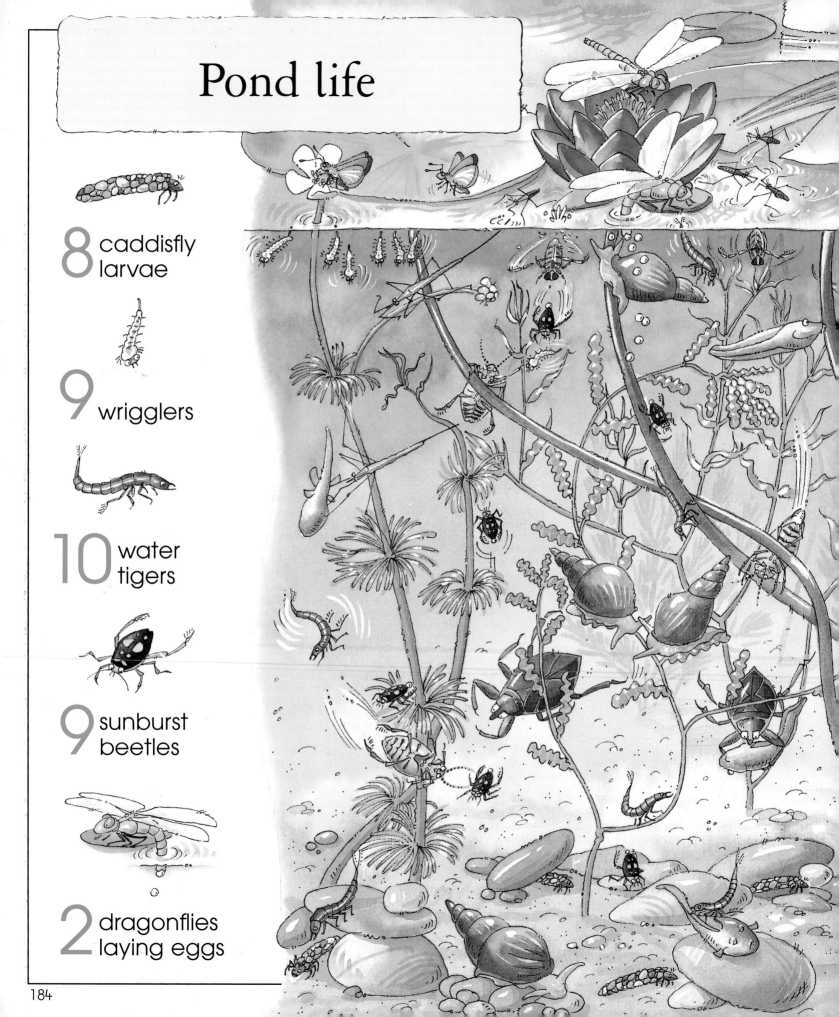

8 caddisfly larvae

9 wrigglers

10 water tigers

9 sunburst beetles

2 dragonflies laying eggs

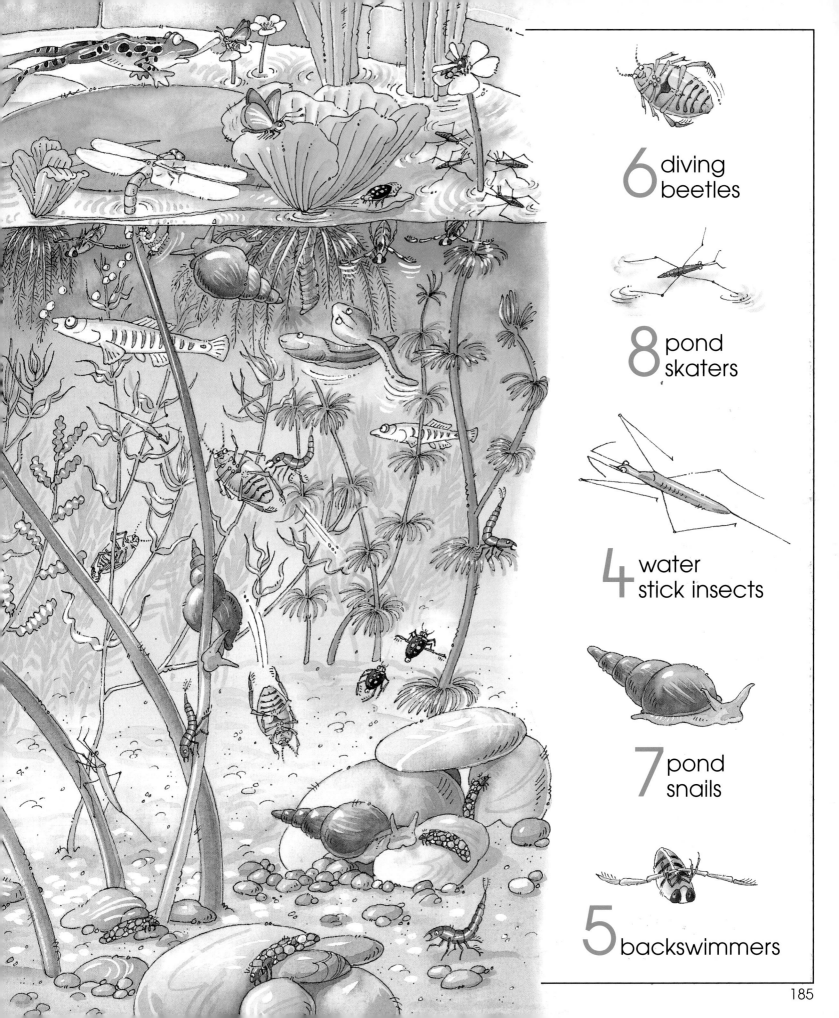

6 diving beetles

8 pond skaters

4 water stick insects

7 pond snails

5 backswimmers

Craggy cave

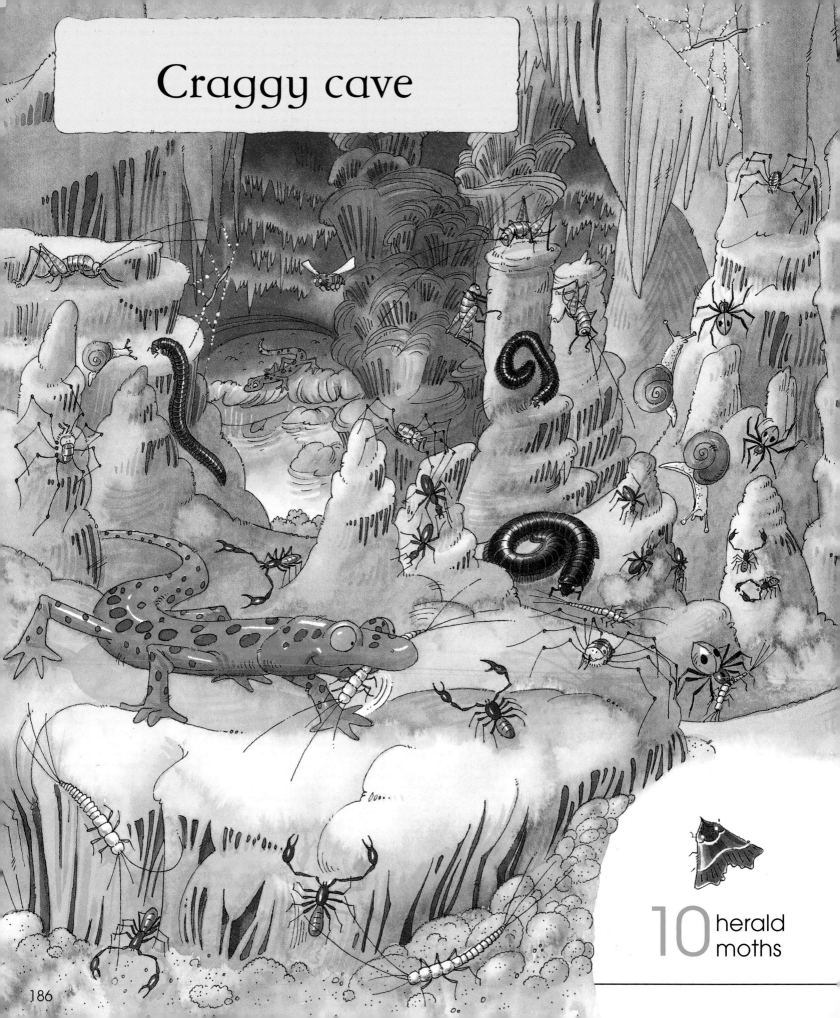

10 herald moths

10 ground beetles

8 harvestmen

6 cave silverfish

5 giant millipedes

9 cave snails

7 camel crickets

4 webworms

5 cave spiders

9 false scorpions

Grassy meadow

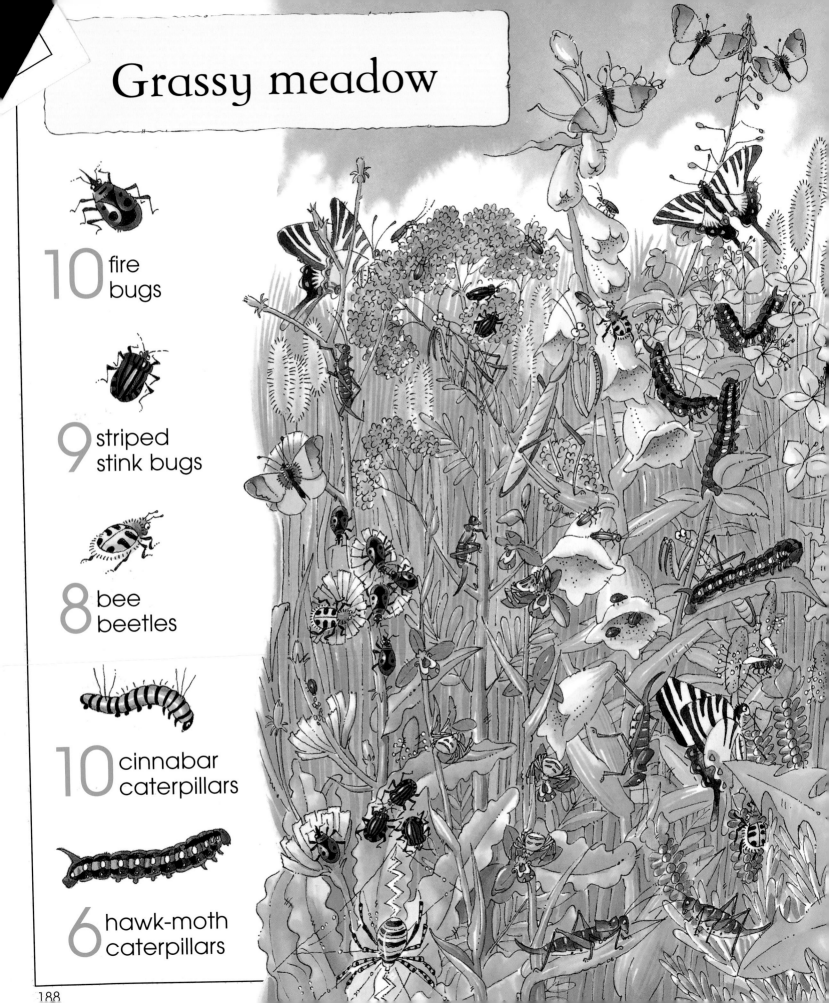

10 fire bugs

9 striped stink bugs

8 bee beetles

10 cinnabar caterpillars

6 hawk-moth caterpillars

5 praying mantises

7 crab spiders

5 wasp spiders

9 bush crickets

7 soldier beetles

Nightlife

6 stag beetles

4 cicadas

9 owl moths

10 weaver ants

7 blue beetles

10 fireflies

8 awlking caterpillars

9 snails with yellow shells

3 slant-faced grasshoppers

7 inchworm moths

Butterfly house

At a butterfly house, you can see butterflies from all around the world. Look back through the scenes of bugs and see if you can find and count all of these butterflies.

5 swordtails

4 zebra butterflies

2 blue morpho butterflies

5 sleepy orange butterflies

6 yellow pansy butterflies

8 orange-tips

4 skipper butterflies

7 swallowtails

2 tortoiseshell butterflies

6 white admirals

5 checkerspots

5 comma butterflies

4 fritillaries

3 brimstones

Answers

Did you find all the butterflies?
Here's where they are.

5 swordtails:
Jungle floor
(pages 178–179)

4 zebra butterflies:
Vegetable patch
(pages 180–181)

2 blue morpho butterflies:
Tropical treetops
(pages 170–171)

5 sleepy orange butterflies:
Rocky desert
(pages 168–169)

6 yellow pansy butterflies:
Sandy desert
(pages 174–175)

8 orange-tips:
Grassy meadow
(pages 188–189)

4 skipper butterflies:
Pond life
(pages 184–185)

7 swallowtails:
Grassy meadow
(pages 188–189)

2 tortoiseshell butterflies:
Underground
(pages 172–173)

6 white admirals:
Leafy woodland
(pages 182–183)

5 checkerspots:
Leafy woodland
(pages 182–183)

5 comma butterflies:
Flowerbed
(pages 166–167)

4 fritillaries:
Garden shed
(pages 176–177)

3 brimstones:
Flowerbed
(pages 166–167)

Managing editor: Gillian Doherty
Managing designers: Laura Fearn
and Mary Cartwright

The publishers would like to thank Carl Cantaluppi,
Horticulture Agent at North Carolina State University
and Dr. Gordon Wardell, President of S.A.F.E. Research
& Development, for their helpful advice.

1001
Things to Spot
on the Farm

Gillian Doherty

Illustrated by Teri Gower

Designed by Susannah Owen

Edited by Kamini Khanduri

Series editor: Felicity Brooks
Series designer: Mary Cartwright
Agricultural educational consultant: Liza Dibble

Contents

Things to spot

These big pictures show different kinds of farms all around the world. On every page there are lots of things for you to find and count. There are 1001 things to spot altogether. The example page below shows what you need to do.

There's a red balloon hidden in each big picture. Can you find them all?

Each little picture shows you what to look for in the big picture.

The blue number shows how many of that thing you need to find.

Milking time

204

3 milking jars

6 cows eating grass

7 goat kids

10 cow bells

2 cows sleeping

3 stools

1 calf feeding

7 milk churns

1 black bull

6 red buckets

205

There's a scarecrow puzzle on page 224.

There are all kinds of things to spot scattered throughout the scenes. You can find out what you need to do to find them all on pages 224–225.

The sheep farm

10 white sheep with black faces   3 dogs   1 shearing machine   8 lambs   10 poppies

9 rabbits

2 pairs of clippers

4 sheep with horns

3 shepherds' crooks

5 black sheep

The fruit farm

6 orange trees

9 birds flying

8 bags of lemons

2 donkeys

5 lemon trees

10 lizards
7 baskets of grapes
2 tractors
7 ladders
3 striped cats

The greenhouse

9 green tomatoes

2 forks

8 red strawberries

4 snails

10 cucumbers

202

10 red tomatoes

2 watering cans

5 caterpillars

7 empty plant pots

2 seed trays

Milking time

3 milking jars

6 cows eating grass

7 goat kids

10 cow bells

2 cows sleeping

3 stools

1 calf feeding

7 milk churns

1 black bull

6 red buckets

Baby animals

10 chicks

1 calf

7 lambs

5 puppies

2 foals

7 clean pink piglets

6 striped kittens

3 muddy piglets

4 black kittens

2 goat kids

Harvest time

1 combine harvester

10 seagulls

1 blue tractor

9 rabbits

10 bales of straw

1 baling machine
9 crows
2 grain trailers
3 red tractors
4 foxes

At the stables

7 saddles

6 bales of hay

5 sponges

2 foals

1 horse trailer

10 riding hats   3 black horses   7 forks   3 horse blankets   6 brown hens

The henhouse

1 fox

7 brown chicks

9 loose feathers

1 egg hatching

5 brown hens

8 mice 10 yellow chicks 2 bowls of grain 10 brown eggs 9 white hens

The rice fields

1 water pump

9 hats

3 kites

10 ducks

7 sacks of rice seeds

 4 water buffaloes

 8 baskets of rice plants

 5 babies in slings

 3 bicycles

 5 black pigs

On the pond

10 ducklings 9 eggs 1 puppy 6 geese 3 birds' nests

5 ducks
swimming

2 duck
houses

7 goslings

6 dragonflies

8 fish

217

On the ranch

9 black cows

2 trucks

3 armadillos

9 cowboy hats

10 cows with horns

8 coils of rope 6 cowboys on horses 7 dogs 9 red bandanas 3 black horses

The honey farm

5 box-shaped beehives

4 smoke machines

5 bars of honey soap

9 pots of honey

3 pairs of white gloves

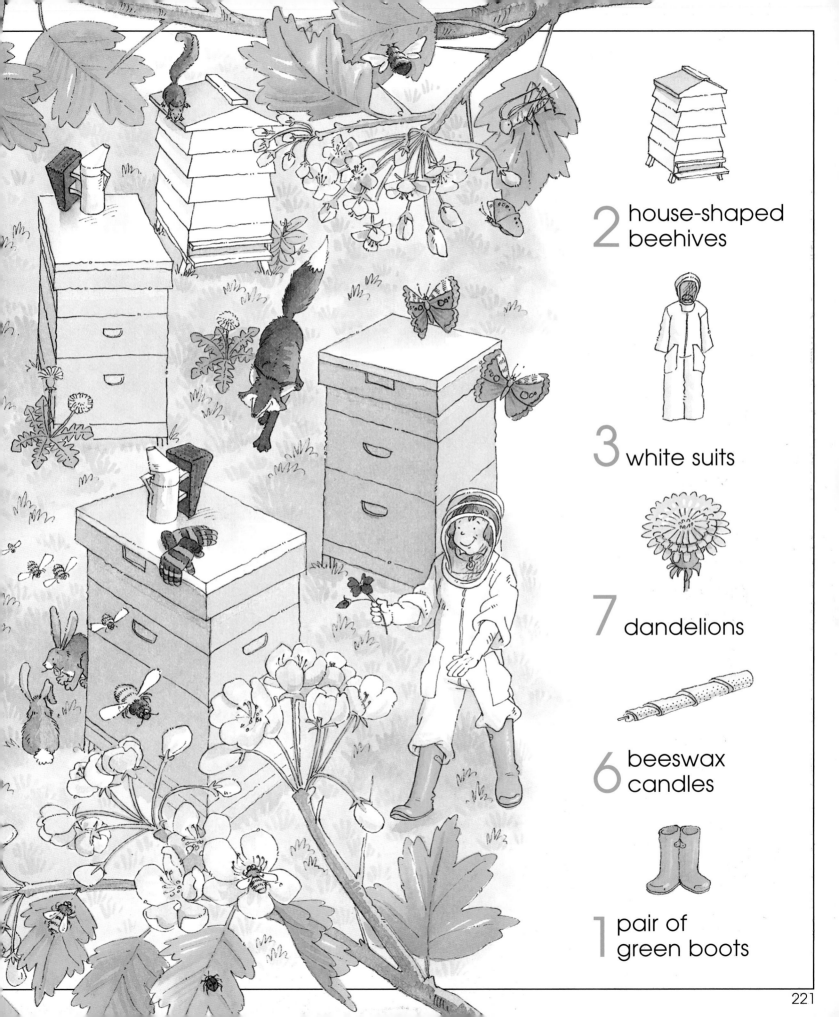

2 house-shaped beehives

3 white suits

7 dandelions

6 beeswax candles

1 pair of green boots

Tropical farm

2 sloths

5 toucans

10 cocoa pods

7 monkeys

8 sacks of coffee beans

4 yellow caps

5 baskets of pineapples

6 coffee bushes

3 snakes

4 bunches of bananas

The scarecrow

This scarecrow is made from things found on the farms in these scenes. Look back and see if you can find which page each thing is from.

Sunflower

Carrot

Blue floppy hat

Pair of striped gloves

Long green coat

Yellow scarf

Spotted handkerchief

Spot 10 mice hiding in the scarecrow's clothes.

The answers are on page 226.

More things to spot

Did you spot any of these things?
Look back through the farm scenes
to see if you can find them all.

4 moles

8 blue butterflies

2 rakes

9 yellow butterflies

2 umbrellas

8 blue buckets

6 wheelbarrows

7 yellow buckets

6 brooms

3 squirrels

4 shovels

9 frogs

There are lots of people in these farm scenes. How many can you spot on each farm? Some of them are small or partly hidden, so you will need to search very carefully. The answers are on page 226.

225

Answers

The scarecrow

The sunflower is on page 201 (The fruit farm).
The carrot is on page 202 (The greenhouse).
The blue floppy hat is on page 207 (Baby animals).
The striped gloves are on page 221 (The honey farm).
The long green coat is on page 198 (The sheep farm).
The yellow scarf is on page 205 (Milking time).
The spotted handkerchief is on page 212 (The henhouse).

More things to spot

Did you manage to spot all the extra things scattered through the farms?
Here's where they all were:

Moles
The sheep farm: 2
Milking time: 1
Harvest time: 1

Blue butterflies
The greenhouse: 1
The henhouse: 1
On the pond: 3
The honey farm: 3

Rakes
Milking time: 1
Baby animals: 1

Yellow butterflies
The greenhouse: 2
The henhouse: 2
On the pond: 2
The honey farm: 3

Umbrellas
The rice fields: 1

On the pond: 1

Blue buckets
Milking time: 2
Baby animals: 1
Harvest time: 1
The henhouse: 1
On the pond: 1
On the ranch: 2

Wheelbarrows
The fruit farm: 1
Baby animals: 1
At the stables: 2
On the ranch: 2

Yellow buckets
Milking time: 3
At the stables: 3
On the pond: 1

Brooms
The sheep farm: 1

Milking time: 2
At the stables: 2
On the ranch: 1

Squirrels
Milking time : 1
At the stables: 1
The honey farm: 1

Shovels
Baby animals: 1
Harvest time: 1
At the stables: 2

Frogs
The greenhouse: 1
Milking time: 1
Baby animals: 2
The henhouse: 1
The rice fields: 1
On the pond: 3

Did you count the people on each farm? Here's how many there were:

The sheep farm: 11
The fruit farm: 32
The greenhouse: 0
Milking time: 10
Baby animals: 0

Harvest time: 22
At the stables: 21
The henhouse: 0
The rice fields: 69

On the pond: 0
On the ranch: 18
The honey farm: 3
Tropical farm: 12

Acknowledgements

The publishers
would like to thank
the following
individuals and
organizations
for providing
information:

Fullwood Ltd,
Dairy Equipment
Manufacturers,
Shropshire, UK

Frances Wood,
Curator of the
Chinese Collections,
British Library,
London, UK

James Hamill,
Beekeeping
Consultant,
The Hive Honey Shop,
London, UK

The Ranching
Heritage Association,
Texas, USA

1001
Things to Spot
in the Town

Anna Milbourne
Illustrated by Teri Gower

Designed by Susannah Owen

Edited by Gillian Doherty
Series editor: Felicity Brooks   Series designer: Mary Cartwright

Additional design: Nicola Butler

Contents

Things to spot

The pictures in this section show scenes from different towns. On every page there are lots of things for you to find and count.

There are 1001 things to spot altogether. The example pages below show what you need to do to find them.

Each little picture shows you what to look for in the big picture.

The blue number tells you how many of that thing you need to find.

This is Sam. She visited each of the towns in the scenes. See if you can spot her in each picture.

Sam took photos of her trip and she brought things back from each town. On pages 256 and 257 you can look at these things and there are two puzzles for you to do.

Street café

3 newspapers

6 trays

8 pieces of cake

7 waiters

10 glasses of juice

9 pigeons

6 parasols

5 ice creams

10 menus

1 musician

Market town

4 donkeys

10 red rugs

8 sacks of spices

10 blue bowls

7 lanterns

9 crates of oranges   2 snakes   3 carts   7 teapots   6 mirrors

Nightlife

9 blue caps

3 hot dog stands

10 cartons of popcorn

4 yellow taxis

6 street lights

 1 ticket seller

 8 drinks with straws

 1 girl running

 3 burger signs

 10 umbrellas

River town

8 baskets of bananas

7 washing lines

2 pots of red flowers

5 tubs of laundry

4 monks

1 ferry

10 straw hats

7 children splashing

6 baskets of rice

9 baskets of peppers

Town square

1 fountain

7 pink arches

10 school bags

9 pigeons flying

4 street artists

10 scooters **1** clock **10** ice creams **4** banners **7** piles of books

Fortress town

3 camels

10 orange turbans

3 elephants

8 bowls of samosas

10 women in pink saris

10 sacks 8 cows 9 flower garlands 1 gateway 10 blue books

Town park

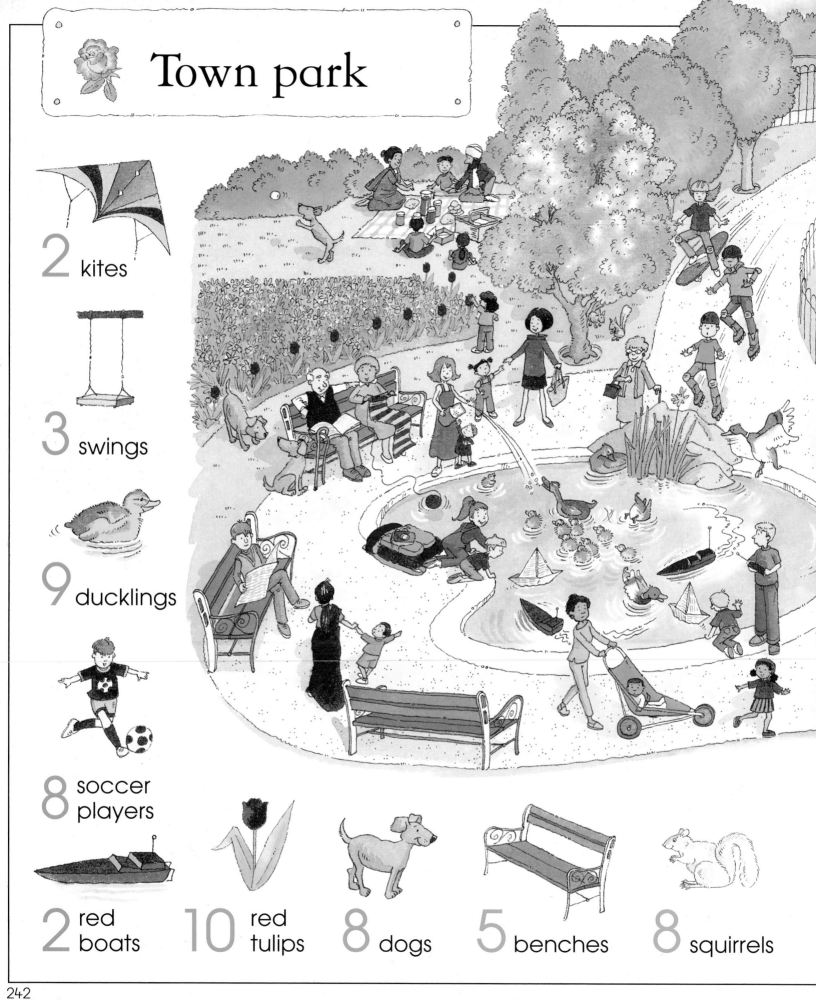

2 kites

3 swings

9 ducklings

8 soccer players

2 red boats

10 red tulips

8 dogs

5 benches

8 squirrels

6 people skating

Traffic jam

8 green taxis

2 road signs

10 bicycles

3 buses

9 brown briefcases

244

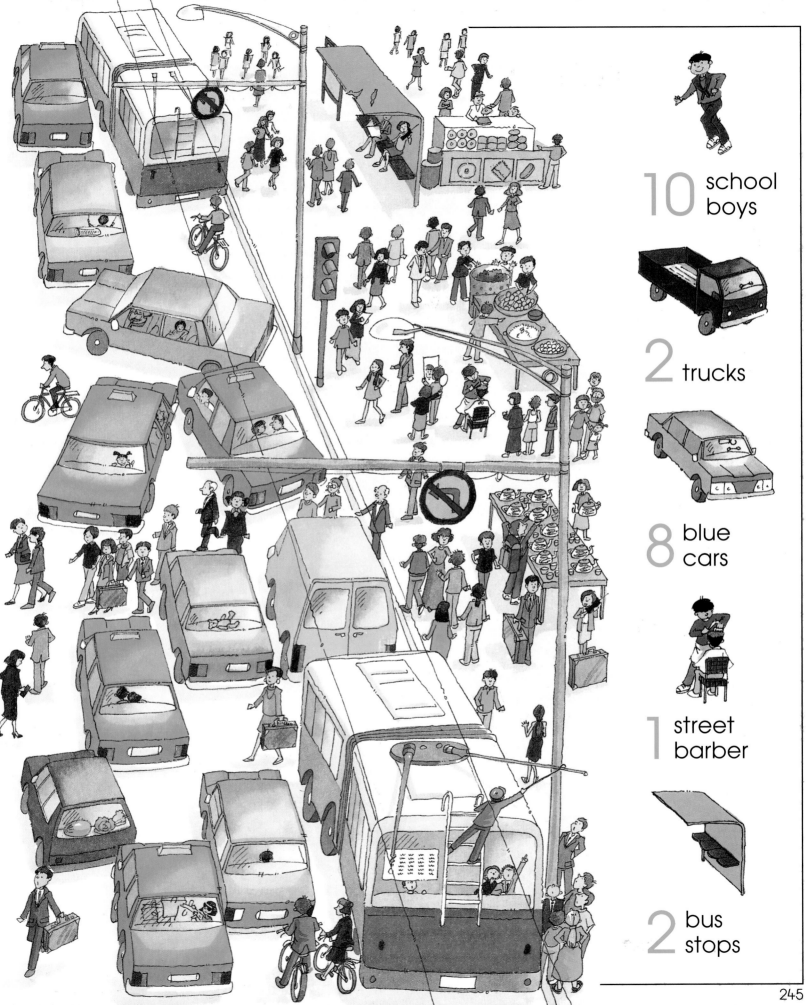

10 school boys

2 trucks

8 blue cars

1 street barber

2 bus stops

Fishing port

8 cats

5 empty buckets

10 seagulls

7 crab pots

3 nets

9 crabs 10 buckets of fish 6 fishermen 2 postcard stands 4 boats

Country village

9 buckets of water

10 soccer players

8 babies in slings

9 women pounding grain

4 children with hoops

9 dishes of mangoes

1 well

10 goats

7 huts

9 striped headscarves

Shopping street

9 skateboards   7 shoeboxes   8 striped T-shirts   10 beach balls   6 swimsuits

9 toy kangaroos   6 jars of lollipops   8 flowery dresses   10 red bags   8 kookaburras

Snowy town

10 blue parkas

1 plane

10 dogs

9 log cabins

5 snowmobiles

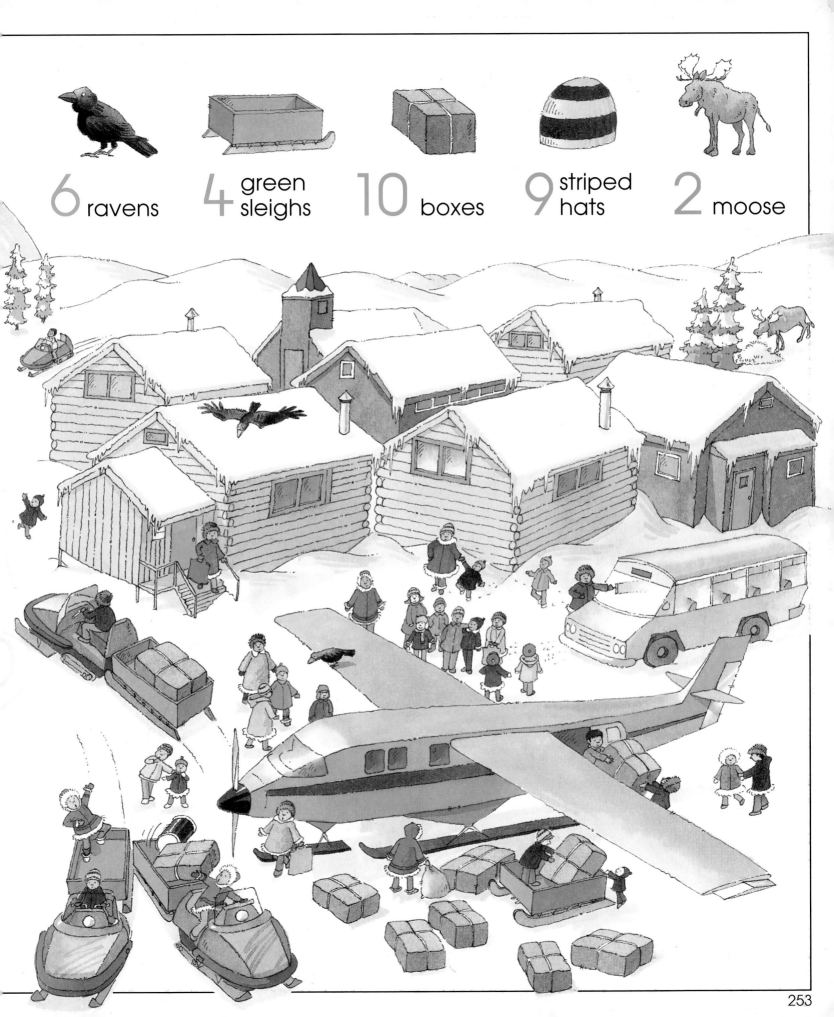

6 ravens

4 green sleighs

10 boxes

9 striped hats

2 moose

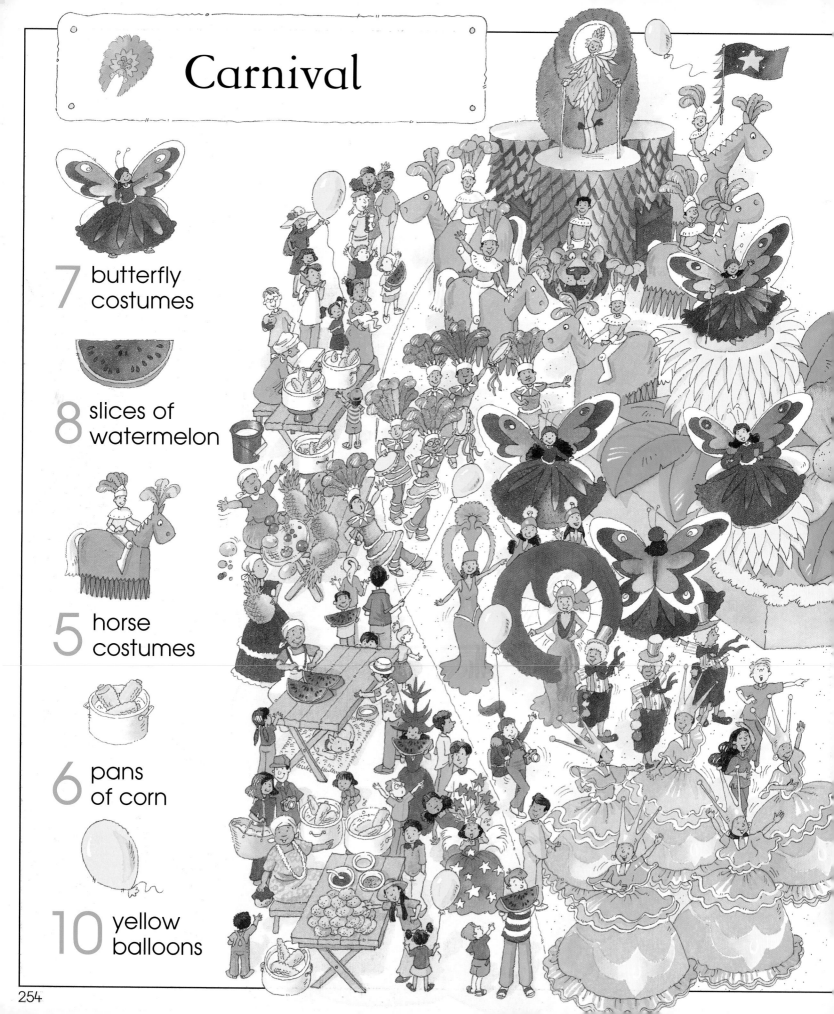

Carnival

7 butterfly costumes

8 slices of watermelon

5 horse costumes

6 pans of corn

10 yellow balloons

254

9 gold crowns 6 drummers 4 pineapples 10 flags 8 clowns

Photos

These are photos that Sam took in the towns she went to. Can you find which scene each photo is from?

Souvenirs

Sam brought these souvenirs back from the towns she visited. Can you find which towns they are from and count them all?

10 blue and white teapots

10 striped bags

4 posters of aliens

10 yellow shells

9 wooden elephants

8 orange feathers

10 brown fur hats

7 starfish

 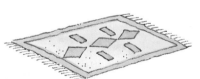  

4 boxes of chocolates

9 yellow rugs

5 cake boxes

10 balloons with faces

3 koras

9 napkins

2 paper boats

9 puppets

Answers

Did you find all the photos and the souvenirs? Here's where they are.

Photos

1 Carnival
(page 255)

2 Town park
(page 243)

3 River town
(page 236)

4 Street café
(page 231)

5 Market town
(page 233)

6 Fortress town
(page 240)

7 Nightlife
(page 235)

8 Fishing port
(page 247)

9 Town square
(page 239)

10 Traffic jam
(page 245)

11 Snowy town
(page 252)

12 Shopping street
(page 250)

13 Country village
(page 248)

Souvenirs

10 blue and white teapots:
Traffic jam
(pages 244 and 245)

10 striped bags:
Shopping street
(pages 250 and 251)

4 posters of aliens:
Nightlife
(pages 234 and 235)

10 yellow shells:
Fishing port
(pages 246 and 247)

9 wooden elephants:
River town
(pages 236 and 237)

8 orange feathers:
Carnival
(pages 254 and 255)

10 brown fur hats:
Snowy town
(pages 252 and 253)

7 starfish:
Fishing port
(pages 246 and 247)

4 boxes of chocolates:
Street café
(pages 230 and 231)

9 yellow rugs:
Market town
(pages 232 and 233)

5 cake boxes:
Street café
(pages 230 and 231)

10 balloons with faces:
Town square
(pages 238 and 239)

3 koras:
Country village
(pages 248 and 249)

9 napkins:
Street café
(pages 230 and 231)

2 paper boats:
Town park
(pages 242 and 243)

9 puppets:
Fortress town
(pages 240 and 241)

Acknowledgements

The publishers would like to thank the following people for providing information about different towns:

Caroline Liou, China
Cheryl Ward, Australia
Daryl Bowers, Barrow, Alaska
Mr Jensen, Dan Fishing
Equipment Ltd., Denmark
Frances Linzee Gordon, Morocco
Helene Kratzsch and Marie Rose
von Wesendonk
Ibrahim Keith Holt, The Council of
the Obsidian, West Africa Office
Imogen Franks, Lonely Planet Publications
Michael Willis, Curator, British Museum
Susannah Selwyn, ES International
Language Schools